THE LUNA

Astrologica. .... .y
Control

Francesca Naish

First published in Australasia in 1989 by
Nature & Health Books
This edition co-published in Great Britain by
Prism Press, 2 South Street, Bridport,
Dorset DT6 3NQ, England
and distributed in the United States of America by
the Avery Publishing Group Inc.,
350 Thorens Avenue, Garden City Park, New York, 11040

ISBN 1 85327 013 X (Prism Press) ISBN 0 94909 913 9 (Nature & Health Books)

Printed by The Guernsey Press, Guernsey, Channel Islands.

CONTENTS

To my children, who turned out even better than I planned, my husband for his care, support and co-operation in having them (and only them) and my mother and father who loved me greatly even though I was their last chance for a son.

ACKNOWLEDGEMENTS

Firstly my great and enduring thanks go to Dr. Jonas, without whom many, many women would today be less healthy and happy, and to Dr. Rechnitz and his other associates. Secondly to Lynn Schroeder and Sheila Ostrander, whose book *Astrological Birth Control* (Prentice-Hall, New Jersey 1972) brought his ideas to a wide public in the west. Then to Art and Judy Rosenblum, authors, editors and publishers of *The Natural Birth Control Book* (Aquarian Research Foundation, Philadelphia), who extended the coverage on the lunar cycle, associated it with other natural birth control methods, and kept the lunar cycle "in print" through their independent publishing.

My thanks go to Rex Matthews and all of the Village Church Community Centre during the time that the community projects there provided a caring and supportive environment for the growth of my practice, and the Healing and Growth Centre that grew around it, and to my friends and colleagues over the years at the Village Healing and Growth Centre, which has been my second home for so long, who have contributed enormously to the growth of my approach to fertility.

My thanks go to Jane Bennett, who has also worked at the Village Healing and Growth Centre, for her time, energy and insight in writing the chapter on further astrological influences on fertility, to Nevill Drury, my publisher, for his enthusiasm, support and patience, to my dear friend Jaqueline Bateman for her wonderful illustrations, to "Captain" Rom Nurio for writing the programme to calculate and print the lunar cycle charts for my clients, to Margaret Lewis, a client of mine who also works in this field, for her input and ideas, and to Denis Stewart and Raymond Khouri who greatly increased my knowledge and love of herbal medicine.

Further thanks go to Paul and Sandra Firnan for the use of their mountain home for my "Writing Retreats" away from the demands of home life, to Margaret Munro for her beach house, to Kim my dog for keeping me faithful (and silent) company, and to Renee Engl for her generous support during this time off from my practice.

Lastly, thanks go to my family for coping with my absences of mind and body as I became absorbed in this project, and to my clients who have provided me with all the experiences necessary for its execution, which took place, incidentally, on a Commodore Amiga 1000.

A NOTE ON THE AUTHOR

Francesca Naish D.C.H., M.A.T.M.S is a qualified hypnotherapist and herbalist who runs a unique naturopathic fertility practice in Sydney, Australia, where she lives with her husband, two children and various animals. Her approach is practical and humorous and comes from her long experience using the techniques discussed in this book over the last 13 years. During this time she has helped over 2,000 women and their partners to find the answers to their fertility problems. She works at the Village Healing and Growth Centre, which grew around her practice, and which now offers a wide range of natural healing modalities, available from a diverse team of therapists. Francesca also offers consultations and workshops in Natural Vision Improvement, in which she was also a pioneer in Australia. As well as her clinical practice, she has helped many women both interstate and internationally with her postal service.

She has appeared often on both radio and television, talking on her speciality subjects of natural methods of fertility awareness and natural vision improvement, written extensively for natural health magazines, been the subject of articles and interviews in the press, lectured at all the natural health training colleges in Sydney, at a nursing training college, and to countless interested groups and conventions.

Having grown up in England, been educated at Godolphin School, Salisbury, and at Sussex University, where she studied mathematics, she went on to work with computers, manage a health food store, and work in both theatre and circus as a mime/clown/comedienne. She extended this work to become involved with children in schools, open spaces and institutions, but on arriving in Australia in her late twenties gave up the theatre in favour of concentrating on her interests in natural health and women. She then changed the emphasis of the natural birth control methods that she had employed for contraception, and planned her family. To join her two step-children came her first child, conceived on Friday the thirteenth (an astrologically auspicious day) and born on April Fool's Day! Her second followed six years later.

For those of you who know a little astrology we include her horoscope. As you can see with her moon, ascendant and Uranus in Gemini (communication) and her sun, Venus and Jupiter in Scorpio (birth, reproduction and sex) and many planets in the sixth house of service, she has (finally) chosen a suitable career!

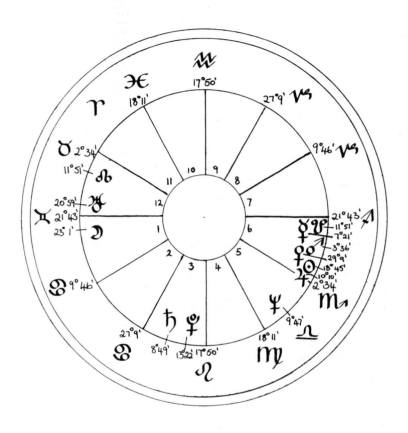

FRANCESCA NAISH
born 6p.m. 11/11/46
BRIGHTON, SUSSEX, ENGLAND.
(0°10′W 50°50′N)

INTRODUCTION

This book has arisen from my experiences putting these ideas into practice both for myself and for my many clients.

My practice arose from my own need for an effective and natural contraception method, and to conceive consciously and in good health. My involvement with astrology and naturopathic healing modalities came together and I added the lunar cycle observances to the other natural birth control methods available at the time. Having successfully used this combination myself for many years, I then made them available to others, and the scope of my practice has grown considerably, in both size and ideas, from its beginning 13 years ago.

For the information on the lunar cycle I originally turned to Sheila Ostrander and Lynn Schroeder's book *Astrological Birth Control* (Prentice-Hall, New Jersey 1972), and later to *The Natural Birth Control Book* (Aquarian Research Foundation, Philadelphia, U.S.A.). Sheila Ostrander and Lynn Schroeder had originally written of Jonas' work on the lunar cycle in their previous book *Psychic Discoveries Behind the Iron Curtain*, and were responsible for bringing his work, and the ideas contained therein, to an appreciative audience in the West.

This book is in no way as extensive in its treatment of Jonas' work as theirs, and although their book is now out of print, it may be available through public libraries, and I would recommend it thoroughly to anyone wishing to study the subject further.

In this book I have attempted to bring the ideas on the lunar cycle together with other natural fertility awareness methods, such as mucous and temperature observations, to give an informed and practical guide and a comprehensive approach.

Both the mucous and temperature methods have been written about fairly extensively, but as far as I know very little has been written on their use in conjunction with the lunar cycle. In my practice I have found that the use of the lunar cycle has increased the effectiveness of the sympto-thermal method, giving the extra "edge" to these methods' success.

My aim has always been to give information, not rules, so that these methods can be adapted to suit all women in all circumstances. With this information a woman can make an informed choice as to how to deal with the various fertility needs that crop up in her life, and adjust these methods accordingly. To that end I have also included guidelines on how to combine the barrier techniques of contraception (diaphragm and condom) with fertility diagnosis, for those who find periodic abstinence too difficult, and some advice on natural methods of treatment for common disorders of the reproductive system (both male and female).

As I have not been able to have direct contact with Dr. Jonas I can but offer my apologies if he is in any way misrepresented here, and can only hope that his work can be extended through this book.

Many "orthodox" practitioners have, in the past, objected to these methods. Objections to "natural" methods have been based on the doubts that some medical personnel have as to a woman's capacity to manage her own reproductive affairs. Whilst I acknowledge that not all women are suitable candidates for these methods, I feel strongly that any woman motivated to use them can do so successfully and should have access to the information that allows her to be independent of the health risks involved in the more commonly prescribed methods of family planning.

Objections to the use of the lunar cycle have often arisen from its title of "Astrological". In fact the lunar cycle is not really "astrological", in that it deals merely with a monthly repeating cycle, and the relationship between only two heavenly bodies, the sun and the moon. In some ways then, the title 'Astrological Birth Control' is a misnomer, and may alienate those who might be prepared to consider the moon cycle's role in influencing fertility. Although we do touch in this book on Astrological influences on fertility, the lunar cycle itself is not based on traditional astrological philosophy, but on empirically proven fact.

I attempt briefly to bring together some of the arguments that I feel may form a basis of a proper scientific understanding of the effect of the lunar cycle. I am only too aware, however, of the areas in which we have, as yet, no answers. If this book could, as well as help women in the practical application of these ideas, stimulate further research into the "why" and "how" of this cycle, I would be thrilled.

I have always intended to undertake a survey of the many women who have attended my practice. Unfortunately, a couple of years ago, my client records were stolen in a burglary at my home. Although I still have the case histories of the many women who saw me before this date, I have no way of contacting them. I would welcome information from them, or any other users of these methods, so that it may be possible to add to the statistical evidence that this cycle is a truly effective part of our understanding of fertility and reproduction.

Although the ideas in this book have worked for large numbers of women, they do rely on informed use to be effective. Responsibility lies with the user to remain aware, and not to abuse the methods. No guarantee can be given of their success in individual cases, though it is with confidence that I present them to you here, with my best wishes for:-

CONFIDENT CONTRACEPTION AND CONSCIOUS CONCEPTION

1 LADY MOON

Throughout the ages the moon has symbolised two things. Firstly it has stood for woman, her femininity, her special characteristics, distinctive from and contrasting with those of man. Secondly it has stood for fertility, reproduction in the animal world, and growth in the kingdom of plants.

The roots of these beliefs about the moon are deep in many cultures and religions, and are invariably connected with an appreciation of the special powers of women.

They occur in many races all over the world including the aboriginal people of Australia, Polynesia and Asia, African negroes, American Indians and even the primitive people of Greenland. The folktales and legends of European peasantry have much "lunar" content, and this is a tradition which extends world-wide.

Religions have centered on the moon in India, China and Mongolia, ancient Greece and Rome, South America, Arabia and Syria, and in the old religions of the Celts in Northern and Western Europe.

It's understandable that such a large and obvious heavenly body should figure strongly in myth and religion, but we find that again and again, in widely dispersed and different cultures, the moon is inseparably connected to woman and fertility. These beliefs have a basis in the experiences and observations of people all over the world from time immemorial.

Most primitive people have considered the moon's influence as necessary for growth. This applies to woman's capacity to bear children, the reproductive ability of animals, and the germination and growth of seeds and plants.

These beliefs may well have been based on observation that the moon's cycles affected fertility and growth, but they were often taken even further.

The moon was seen by some as the fertilising power, actually giving life to a previously inert substance. The primitive tribes of Greenland believe that it is the moon that impregnates women, and women there protect themselves by rubbing saliva on their bellies, to prevent them swelling, before looking at the moon or sleeping on their backs.

Conversely in some cultures women wishing to conceive would sleep with their bellies exposed to the light of the full moon, and in Brittany it is believed that conception is likely to occur if a woman exposes her lower body to a new or "horned" moon.

In Nigeria the Moon Mother is seen as sending the moonbird to earth bringing babies to women who have no need of husbands for procreation, a similar myth to our own baby-bringing stork.

The Maories of New Zealand believe that the moon is the true husband of all women. This is an interesting variation on the perceived sex of the moon though not on its special relationship with women, evident in the belief they have that women all menstruate with the new moon.

Many other tribes have similar beliefs. For some, man's only function is to rupture the hymen, whereby he makes way for the fertilising moonbeam to enter the womb, and others consider him completely irrelevant to the act of conception.

The moon is known as influencing birth as well as conception. In Western Asia the crescent moon symbol was once worn as a charm to bring children to the family, and in southern Italy it is worn to bring the Moon Mother's help in childbirth. These Catholic women identify the Virgin Mary as the Christian embodiment of the Moon Mother.

The special relationship of women, the moon and growing things, was often manifested in primitive peoples by giving the women charge over the cultivation of the crops, which were of course sown and harvested at certain phases of the moon.

The germination and growth of plants was seen to have a relationship with these phases, and women as having a monthly or lunar cycle of bleeding. This could result in menstrual blood being thought itself to have properties of fertility, and being used as a fertiliser for plants.

Beliefs such as these, although primitive and in some respects foreign to scientifically sophisticated levels of understanding, must be perceived as perhaps tuning in to more subtle levels of energetic influence than modern science has yet recognised, and certainly as arising from observable truth.

Indeed modern research bears out the idea that different phases of the moon have varied influences on plant growth. Both Hauschka in Germany and Louis C. Kervran in France, experimenting with seeds germinated at different phases of the moon, found remarkable differences in metabolism of calcium phosphate and other elements depending on the phase present at germination.

The waxing moon is commonly held to coincide with the period of growth for all things, and the waning moon to be the time to gather a harvest and prepare the ground for the next planting.

These beliefs are still part of agricultural practice today in many less "developed" societies, and are being increasingly used by those who feel the need to tune into nature's cycles rather than basing their confidence in their ability to overcome them.

We may conclude that the absence of such practices in modern agriculture has more to do with this perhaps misplaced confidence in modern technology to override nature, than in any greater understanding of the presence or absence of natural fertility cycles.

The effect of the moon on breeding cycles is also demonstrated clearly in

animal life. Many different forms of marine life, worms, fish, some types of seaweed and even coral, breed with specific phases of the moon.

The Pacific Palolo worms breed at the last quarter moon of October and November. In Bermuda the full moon in the spring sees swarms of small luminous fireworms rising to the surface of the sea to perform breeding rituals. Conversely a local species of shrimp always breeds at the new moon.

The previously held belief that it was the tides that gave rise to these patterns was altered when Dr. Frank Brown of the Northwestern University in Evanston Illinois, U.S.A. experimented by removing some oysters from their home in Long Island Sound to his laboratory in Evanston.

To begin with these oysters continued to open and shut to synchronise with the tides where they had come from, but within two weeks they were responding to the moon in their new environment, where there was no water.

He continued to experiment with vegetables such as potatoes and carrots, with salamanders and worms, and he found that even though they were kept in a changeless environment, their metabolic activity was related to the lunar day. Similar results were achieved with rats and mice.

Dr. Eugen Jonas of Czechoslovakia, whose work we shall be looking at in much detail in the next chapter, asked:-

"Up to the present, science has recognised the influence of the moon on lower order animals. This influence affects their capacity for existence and reproduction ... This possibility has not yet been investigated with respect to man. *However, should the possibility that the moon affects the reproductive function of man be completely excluded?* ... The unicellular ovum of the mother's womb in no way differs from the most minute living creatures which are so strongly affected by the moon. On this basis it no longer appeared impossible to establish a correlation between the influences of the moon and the reproductive ability of man."

Then Jonas claims "After several years of research, it was possible to demonstrate this connection."

3

There has always been much belief in the moon's influence over the menstrual cycle of women.

The North American Indians, and peasants in some parts of Europe saw the moon as "menstruating". The very word "menstruation" means "moon change" derived from the Latin "mens" or moon (the Greek word for moon is "Mene").

Robert Briffault, in his work "The Mothers", demonstrates many examples of this connection. The Maori term for menstruation is "Mata marama" meaning "Moon sickness", and the moon is believed to have triggered the menarche or beginning of menstruation by touching the girl in her sleep. The Papuans believe that a period is the result of intercourse between the moon and the girl.

German peasants call menstrual bleeding "The moon" and the French "The time of the moon". The Mandigo, the Susus and the Congolese have the same words for both moon and menstruation, "Carro" for the Mandigo and "Njonde" in the Congo. Similarly for the Torres Strait Islanders and the Indians there is a single word with the double meaning of moon and menstrual blood.

Pliny deals at length with the connection between menstruation and the moon, whose periodic waxing and waning ". . . controlled the blood of humans and the sap of plants."

In 1898 Arrhenius reported that the onset of 11,807 periods peaked on the eve of new moon and was more frequent during the waxing than the waning moon. More recently, Gutman and Oswald found one peak of menstrual onset at full moon and another at new moon. Walter and Abraham Menaker show that the mean length of the menstrual cycle is 29.5 days, which is also the length of the mean lunar month, rather than the more widely accepted 28 day cycle. This is corroborated by Dr. Winnifred Berg Cutler of the University of Pennsylvania in her findings.

The Maoris have another belief which is interesting in the light of the more personally specific moon cycles hypothesised by Dr. Jonas. An old Maori woman claimed that "A woman is always affected at the same stage of each moon."

It seems that the moon affects natural phenomena in four main ways. Firstly through its gravitational pull on fluids and secondly by the changing amount of light it shines on the earth. The third effect is less well known, but it appears that the moon influences atmospheric ionisation, the electrical charging of atoms. Positive ions, which for example build up prior to a storm, are notorious for their deleterious effect on mental and physical health, causing a stuffy, headachy and faint feeling of listlessness and ill-ease. Negative ions, as generated by ionisers and which are prevalent after a storm or near the sea, cause a feeling of physical and psychological well-being. Full moon is supposed to bring an increase in positive ions, and the negative ions increase as the moon wanes.

This may have something to do with the time-honoured tradition of "lunatics" — people whose behaviour becomes erratic and moody at full moon and the tendency of mental patients' symptoms to become aggravated at this time.

However we also know that the light of the full moon increases, via the hypothalamus and the pituitary glands, levels of the follicle stimulating hormone (F.S.H.), and that light is absorbed, via the optic nerve, as a nutrient for the body, especially the endocrine system. (These ideas are looked at more fully in Chapter 3, where we explore the synchronicity of cycles.) The pineal gland has also been shown to be responsive to light. The emotional states of women, and their nervous disorders, are well known to have a symbiotic relationship with their hormonal levels, so these two effects of the moon may well be inter-related.

The fourth effect of the moon cycle, that of electro-magnetic charges, may also affect not only nervous states, but also ovulation. Harold Burr and Leonard Ravitz, whose work I shall cite again in Chapter 3, found that firstly there were variations in electrical potential of organisms (including the human body) at new and full moons, a huge increase in women at the time of ovulation, and also in mental patients at times of extreme agitation, notably again the new and full moons (see Chapter 3).

The gravitational effect of the moon on fluids is obvious in the tidal flows, and its effect on fluid content in animal life has been demonstrated. Who are humans to suppose that the essentially fluid release of menstruation is less affected?

Whether the controlling factor of the moon over the menstrual cycle is the gravitational pull, the increase in light, the ionisation of the atmosphere, the changes in electro-magnetic conditions or, more probably, a combination of all of these and perhaps other effects, is not known, but as the ancients and primitive peoples in touch with nature have all known, and as science is finding out, this connection is obvious and undeniable.

Briffault says that calling the moon "the true husband of women" is one fundamental statement of the relationship of women with the moon in their monthly cycles. Another way of seeing this relationship is identifying the moon as the great mother herself.

In this guise she has been worshipped in many religions as Hecate, Isis, Ishtar, Artemis, Demeter and Cybele, one form of the Magna Dea, the great goddess of the moon in Chaldea. As Mary she is seen to be the mother of God. Her worship has related to the moon's phases as seen in the menstrual cycle. Where religions have celebrated these different phases, these ceremonies have frequently been associated with women and reproduction and there are many "superstitions" surviving where women's power is seen as having lunar sources.

In contrast to these celebrations of the power of women and the moon is the practice in other societies of placing a taboo on certain activities of menstruating women, notably preparation of food, sexual intercourse and social activities. This is sometimes thought of as originating in the idea that they are unclean and dangerous and may infect people and objects with which they come into contact. For example, according to Pliny, if a man had intercourse with a woman whilst she was bleeding, and if this coincided with the new moon, ". . . at such seasons sexual intercourse brings death and disease upon a man."!

It has been suggested that this "patriarchal" interpretation may have further originated from the recognition that at the time of menstruation a woman was in touch with magic or psychic powers, a connection made much of by Don Juan in the books by Carlos Casteneda. This contact gave her a psychological need for withdrawal at this time which required that she be allowed solitude.

It has been shown that there is a decrease in the senses of sight, smell, hearing and colour discrimination at menstruation, and that there is a corresponding increase in the internal 'senses' of the body.

The sabbath has its origin in the "Sabbatu", the menstruation of the Babylonian goddess Ishtar, taking place at full moon, at which time no work was done, no cooked food eaten and no journeys undertaken. "Sa-bat" means "heart-rest", the day of rest that the moon takes when full, when neither increasing nor decreasing.

The rest taken by Goddess and women alike from normal duties at this time of menstruation, in order to fulfil psychic and physical needs is one we are completely out of touch with today. Modern woman is presumptive enough to consider herself immune from "primitive" natural cycles, and attempts to keep normal activity going without recognition of their influences. Maybe we can see here one cause of the widespread suffering these days of the premenstrual syndrome and menstrual distress, which could perhaps be seen partially as the result of woman being out of touch with her cyclical nature and needs, physical, psychological and psychic.

The old ways of acknowledging women's cycles were religious and firmly embedded in social customs. Today we need to fulfil these needs individually. The modern woman's opportunity to tune into her physical self and her cycles involves personal exploration, observation and understanding of her sexuality and reproductive functions.

Sexual Freedom has been seen since the advent of modern contraception such as the pill and the I.U.D. as being the freedom to express oneself sexually under all conditions and at all times. Women have been educated recently to believe that they should not only experience this, but provide it, and men to expect it.

Whilst joyful and uninhibited sexual expression is certainly both beneficial and desirable, sexual freedom might perhaps be better defined as the freedom to express oneself sexually without detriment to one's physical or psychological health, and in tune with natural cycles, both personal and planetary.

To this end a woman's understanding of her reproductive cycles, and how to tune into them for purposes of fertility awareness and acknowledgement of physical, psychological and psychic patterns, can be immensely rewarding.

An understanding of the hormonal cycle can bring a chance for a woman to feel in control of her own fertility and in touch with herself physically through observance of her bodily changes, as we shall explore in later chapters.

A further understanding of how the fertility cycle is influenced by the moon not only increases her chances of achieving or preventing pregnancy but also extends this into her opportunity to acknowledge her contact with, and her part in, the corner of the universe in which she dwells.

This book is written in the hope of giving each woman a chance to make her life more meaningful and joyous in terms of her relationship with herself, her partner and her world.

2   THE LUNAR PHASE CYCLE

Eugen Jonas, a psychiatrist with an understanding of astrology (or as he preferred to call it, cosmobiology), had a fairly unique combination of skills and interests for a doctor practising in Czechoslovakia in the mid 1950s, however it was precisely this combination that resulted in his discovery of the lunar phase cycle of fertility. Though he was himself unable to work with this information for more than a short period of time, his discovery has been inspirational to many others all over the world.

As a young medical student in 1947 Jonas had "discovered" astrology by accident in the library of the university where he studied. His interest grew and although his career was in psychiatry, astrology remained sufficiently important for him to be the subject which he looked to for answers to a number of problems that started to worry him in the mid-fifties.

At this time nearby Hungary legalised abortion. As Jonas lived very close to the border and mixed socially with the Hungarians he became involved with the issue and its probable effects. Most of the patients in his predominantly Roman Catholic practice were still using the rhythm method of birth control, with characteristically little success, and he could see how widespread abortion practice could become. In fact the high failure rate of the rhythm method was one of the reasons for the legalisation of abortion in Hungary.

Being a Roman Catholic himself Dr. Jonas did not agree with abortion on ethical grounds, and indeed as a doctor he recommended surgery only when absolutely necessary. He was also concerned with the harmful psychological effects of terminations on his patients.

During his practice as a psychiatrist Dr. Jonas had been extremely troubled by the many mental and physical disturbances and handicaps in the children that he treated, and he now asked himself if it was possible that some of the reasons for these conditions might be connected to astrological influences, particularly those surrounding conception. He had also noticed cyclical emotional changes in women patients which appeared unrelated to the pre-menstrual syndrome, and heightened sexuality in some nervously sensitive women on a thirty day interval unrelated to the menstrual cycle.

As we have explored in Chapter 1, there is both an ancient and modern acceptance of the idea that the moon is connected with fertility, and also with nervous response. All of this was in his mind as he set out to research why the rhythm method was so unsuccessful, and if it could be improved upon, thus increasing the chances of avoiding both abortion and the unnatural methods of contraception being experimented with at the time.

Jonas believed that if the moon could influence the lower order animals, as was recognised by science, then perhaps it could also affect the unicellular ovum and thereby woman's reproductive function. He also felt that if there was any truth in the ancient ideas of astrologers that man and universe were part of the same harmonic unity, then as important an event as conception must indeed be subject to these same cosmic laws.

He discovered a single statement that started him on a whole new journey. From the writings of the ancient astrologers of Babylon and Assyria he unearthed the following:- "Woman is fertile during a certain phase of the moon". He wrote "This Assyrian-Babylonian assertion came down to us as a fragment, only one sentence, which is of no use whatsoever, since no indication was ever found as to which phase of the moon it referred to."

However it was enough to start him looking. He studied, calculated and worked to find the patterns. He drew up many horoscopes for conception times, and checked these and the corresponding natal horoscopes of the mothers for lunar phase clues.

"It took several weeks, days and nights, until on August 15 1956 I finally arrived at the first three fundamental rules on conception, the determination of sex, and life capability of the foetus, all of which can be precisely formulated."

These are the three rules which were the foundation of his work:-

1. The time of a woman's fertility depends on the recurrence of the angle between the sun and the moon that occurred at the woman's own birth. In other words a woman is fertile at the same phase of the moon that she was born at, e.g. a woman born three days after full moon will experience fertility three days after each full moon *regardless of where this falls in her menstrual cycle.*

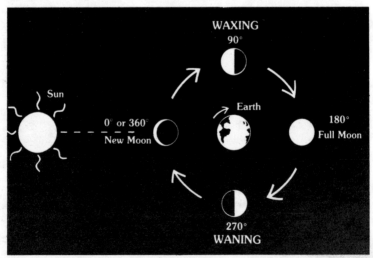

2. The sex of the child conceived depends on the position of the moon at the moment of conception. This echoes the traditional belief that a child born when the moon is in a "male" or positive sign of the zodiac will be male and vice versa.

3. Certain configurations of the nearer celestial bodies and the resulting unfavourable distribution of gravitational forces at the time of conception can affect the viability of pregnancy and foetus.

Rule number one is the basis of what we now call the lunar phase cycle, or the lunar fertility cycle. Jonas had discovered a secondary fertility cycle, starting at the moment of birth, repeating on a lunar interval and becoming effective at puberty. It is this cycle, and the use of it for conception and contraception, that we shall be exploring in this book. It is also this aspect of his discoveries which has received most attention world wide, and therefore been tested most thoroughly. His other ideas, as put forward in rules 2 and 3, although initially checked out fairly thoroughly by Dr. Jonas himself, have not been so extensively used. We shall look at them in detail in Chapter 8.

Dr. Jonas was amazed by the patterns he had uncovered, but could not ignore what appeared to be indisputable fact. He set out to verify his findings.

By checking Bratislava maternity clinic's records of 250 births and the corresponding birth dates of the mothers he found an 87% correlation between the actual sex of the child and his calculations from the data.

In order to do this he calculated the phase of the moon the mother was born at, when this repeated in the month the baby was conceived (i.e. when it would have been conceived if this had occurred on the lunar phase cycle) and what sign the moon was in at the time. In 217 out of 250 cases the results coincided. However further identification proved to be more difficult. "Gynaecologists usually know absolutely nothing about astronomy and astronomers usually know absolutely nothing about gynaecology. Both recoil in horror at the thought of astrology." Jonas' observation would still be true today, and meant that there was for many years no-one either qualified or willing to test his ideas.

In 1957 he received the support of Dr. Jiri Malek, eminent gynaecologist and obstetrician, university professor and doctor in Prague's first maternity clinic, as a representative of the Czechoslovakian Academy of Sciences, to which Jonas had submitted his data.

This support however, though giving official sanction to his continuing studies, still gave him no finances and no facilities. At last in 1960 he was granted paid leave of absence from his psychiatric work and went to Bratislava maternity hospital to test out his theories. He worked as before by correlating actual and calculated sex of the child, and came up with answers that were correct in 94% of the cases.

He also studied data on 8,000 births from 4 maternity hospitals to see if his rule No 3, on viability, bore out. Of these births 112 were classified as non-viable, resulting in sometimes severe deformities. Again his calculations seemed to conform to actual reality. Another survey in a Bratislava maternity hospital and the maternity wings of the hospital in Nitra had Jonas predicting the sex of the child *before* birth. In this survey of 100 cases he was correct in 83.

At this point Dr. Kurt Rechnitz, who was to become largely instrumental in the application of these theories, entered the scene. As director of the women's clinic in the University of Budapest in Hungary he became involved in checking Dr. Jonas' data. He had become aware of Jonas' theory as early as 1956, and he had long had an interest in possible patterns of time of conception, the sex of the child, and fertility generally. He was also concerned to find viable natural methods of contraception.

He applied Jonas' ideas independently and found an 87% success in sex selection. Other tests on sex selection ordered by Dr. Jiri Malek had also come up with a rate of 83%. Although all of these early tests were focused on the ideas embodied in rule No 2, that of determining the sex of the child, they also took into account the ideas of rule No 1, and assumed that conception had occurred when the sun/moon angle present at the mother's birth (the "natal" angle) had repeated. Dr. Rechnitz had also found that in the 15% of his cases where the predicted and actual sex of the child differed, there was a connection with the moon sign present at ovulation as calculated by the rhythm method.

These results got Jonas his first public hearing when he gave a lecture at the first national conference on biological rhythms in Prague at the Academy of Science.

However scientific response was predictably hostile and uninterested, and this trend continued though his ideas became more widely known, being taken seriously by scientists in West Germany, the U.S.S.R., Austria and Hungary, some of whom checked and corroborated his data, others even running checks of their own to support his theories. Popular interest also increased, and appeals from women in Hungary, East and West Germany and Czechoslovakia for help in birth control, fertility problems and sex selection were responded to free of charge.

As a result of this popular interest Jonas got his first chance to test his ideas on birth control. In 1965, at the suggestion of the Czech Academy of Science in Prague, a daily newspaper in Bratislava named "Smena" hosted a symposium of psychiatrists, sociologists and gynaecologists to debate the Jonas theories, and then used the reports of these proceedings and a concurrent series on the ideas to recruit volunteers for a medically supervised test. This test was however abandoned when medical authorities stepped in with objections, but enthusiastic public response simply rerouted itself to Jonas personally. When a West German and an Hungarian paper followed suite, Jonas had an enormous number of requests from people wishing to take part.

His medical superiors then insisted that it was Jonas the astrologer *or* Jonas the psychiatrist. They would no longer permit him to practise psychiatry unless he stopped "meddling" in astrology.

However in the true up and down tradition of Jonas' career, permission was then given by the communist party authority for another paper to run a series of articles and ask for volunteers. This test progressed with 60 couples taking part for a year, and the paper, having analysed the results at the end of that time, published a result of 96% success. Jonas had meanwhile taken advantage of the previous responses to come up with other supportive results of his own.

This led to officials giving Jonas permission to spend half of his working days for six months on astrological research. In this period he drew up 2,000 charts for people who had contacted him.

Yet another paper, more influential, decided to run a survey. Of a starting sample of 470 couples, 293 stayed in the program for 6 months and returned their questionnaires, and of these 36 were eliminated, leaving 257. Only 5 unwanted pregnancies occurred.

Dr. Kurt Rechnitz had by this time adapted Jonas' birth control program to account for the menstrual cycle by incorporating the rhythm method for determining the time of ovulation. Originally Jonas had believed that he had found the *only* fertile time available to a woman. According to Astra International, a private clinic in Vienna where Jonas' ideas are employed, if the ovulation cycle is disregarded completely, and abstinence only occurs on the lunar phase fertile days, contraception is still 80-85% reliable. However in partnership with Dr. Rechnitz, a gynaecologist, the Jonas method was adapted to make allowance for *two* fertile times in a month. We shall look at the significance of these ideas more fully in Chapter 3. Rechnitz' tests of the combined methods in his clinic in Budapest gave 98% results for birth control. He also found that the majority of conceptions (up to 85%) seemed to occur at the lunar phase time rather than the hormonal cycle's ovulation time. However these figures were arrived at by checking backwards through hospital records, and were taken from couples who were predominantly Roman Catholic and may well have been practising the rhythm method, thus making conception on the hormonal cycle less likely. In fact surveys undertaken in the U.S.A. more recently do not bear out these figures, showing a predominance of conceptions occurring at the hormonal cycle ovulation.

Jonas continued to receive a mixed reception of scepticism, hostility and acclaim. The hostility generally outweighed the acclaim, except in popular circles, with Jonas temporarily being refused permission to take his psychiatry examinations, and his own mental health being impugned. Ministries and governments became involved, but nothing was resolved.

Popular support, as expressed through the newspaper "Pravda", coupled with support from local party and health officials, and the paper that had sponsored the practical tests, won the day at last and the "'Astra" clinic, centre for planned parenthood, was established at Nitra with Jonas as director and many resources available to extend the work.

The centre offered calculations to assist four categories of need.

1. Calculation of the sterile days on which no conception can take place.

2. Calculation of the days on which the conception of a boy or girl may be expected in accordance with the wishes of the married couple.

3. Calculation of the days of increased susceptibility to conception in the case of women for whose sterility no medical reason has been given.

4. Calculation of the days on which a healthy child may be expected to be conceived.

In the first six months Astra processed over 9,000 applications for "cosmograms", 2,300 of which were for birth control. At the end of this period in January 1969 the board evaluated data received from 1,600 women using the birth control method over 4 months. The result was 98.5% effective.

Although birth control was the use of the method that Astra tested most thoroughly, the use that was most widely requested was for infertility, and those least requested were for sex selection and conception of viable children. All categories achieved excellent results.

Dr. Rechnitz in his practice in Budapest obtained very good results for infertility, but again no official estimate was made, due to the small numbers involved. However he claimed almost 100% success for sex selection, and 98.2% for birth control.

Many scientists with an interest in Astrology gathered around the centre in Nitra. A board was set up to re-establish astrology, or cosmobiology as they preferred to call it, as a respectable science. Cosmobiology as opposed to astrology is not concerned with analysis or interpretation of symbols, merely with demonstrable and physical effects of certain planetary relationships.

In 1970 Astra's scientific board evaluated the experience of 1,252 women who had used the Jonas/Rechnitz method for a full year. They issued the following report:

"We the undersigned members of the Scientific Council of the Birth Control Research Centre ASTRA, have examined 1252 appraisable cases which occurred between July and December 1968 and which participated in the test for twelve months.

The questionnaires returned were signed by the women participating in the test. Their answers confirmed the reliability or unreliability of the method.

We have found that out of the 1252 cases examined, 1224 could be positively appraised, and only 28 cases proved negative. That means that the reliability of the method, during a test period of twelve months, reaches 97.7%, which corresponds to 2.2 in Pearl's index.

At the same time it should be born in mind that this is *a completely physiological method against which there can be no counterindications* on the medical side, and which are impeccable also from a moral and religious point of view. It may be assumed that the balance of the cases calculated, amounting to several thousand, will also give a positive result.

We, the undersigned, declare that we have made this statement after a careful assessment of the material on hand." *Budapest, April 11, 1970.* (Signed) Dr. K. Rechnitz (Associate Professor), Helene Fazik A.M., Dr. Stephen Dobsa, Dr. Eugene Jonas, Dr. Barna Balogh.

As if all the statistics quoted so far were not convincing enough that Jonas had discovered something important about female fertility, there are several other points which back them up.

1. Many, if not most, of the pregnancies reported in the above test were in women whose menstrual cycle was irregular and who were relying on the rhythm method for calculating when ovulation occurred. Since the rhythm method relies on regularity to work, it is very likely that these conceptions occurred at ovulation.

2. A (small) survey carried out in the U.S.A., instigated by the Aquarian Research Foundation, comes up with similar effective rates for the birth control programme.

3. In instances where women are either trying to conceive, or are in touch with their bodies (for example through using other natural birth control methods involving body awareness), and are fairly unstressed, there is a marked trend towards the hormonal cycle ovulation occurring at the lunar phase fertile time. We will look at this further in Chapter 3.

4. The rhythm method, which is used in these tests, has a success rate when used on its own which has been evaluated as low as 30%. These findings are based on a study of 2,300 American and Canadian women carried out by a medical team headed by Dr. Franklin Brayer in 1969. This is a great deal different from 98%. Nowadays we may use the ovulation and temperature (sympto-thermal) methods instead of the rhythm method and can be confident of even greater success.

5. The Aquarian Research Foundation of Pennsylvania U.S.A. claim in their book *The Natural Birth Control Book* that when a woman is using the contraceptive pill in the "proper" manner then conceptions (or "failures"), are almost always the result of sexual intercourse during the peak lunar phase fertile time.

Although there are many questions to be asked and answers still to come about the "how" and the "why" of Jonas' discoveries, which we shall explore in the next chapter, empirical evidence does seem to overwhelmingly demonstrate its validity. I have found over and over again in my own practice that conceptions do occur at the natal lunar phase recurrence, even when it is virtually impossible for this to have coincided with ovulation on the hormonal cycle.

It seems that much of the opposition in medical and scientific circles to accepting Jonas' theories comes from the association with astrology. However in a sense to call this method "Astrological Birth Control" is a misnomer. It really only has to do with the phases of the moon. His ideas on viability as set out in rule number 3 may have more to do with astrology in that more planets are taken into account, but here again, as Jonas was careful to show, "Cosmobiology", as he preferred to call it, was basically a scientific approach to understanding the effects of the planets and their relationships, and drew very little (if at all except for clues) on traditional, or even modern, interpretive astrology, which is used for purposes as varied as fortune telling and personal growth.

Jonas may not himself be working with these ideas any longer, but many other people are. His systems of birth control and sex selection continued to be used in Hungary, Austria, The United States of America, Italy, The Netherlands, England, Sweden, Canada and Australia, and studied in Yugoslavia, U.S.S.R., Germany, Switzerland and Malaysia. There may be people in many other countries who have heard of and use his ideas. I know that I receive requests for my postal birth control service, which offers calculated lunar phase charts as part of a fertility awareness package (see Chapter 10), from countries all over the world. Most women know that their cycles are connected to the moon and find nothing strange in his ideas. Perhaps if science and medicine were less male-dominated there might be less resistance!

However one man who has embraced Jonas' ideas is E.R. Schweighart of Vienna who has continued using the lunar phase cycle at his clinic Astra International in Vienna. In a communication with Lynn Schroeder and Sheila Ostrander, authors of *Astrological Birth Control*, he said "As far as we are concerned the moon phase theories of Dr. Jonas and Professor Rechnitz have already become repeated facts. We feel it is almost incidental whether these facts will be universally accepted or rejected. Perhaps it is up to the next generation to handle this. In the course of human history it has often happened that new knowledge collides with prevailing world outlooks."

I heartily agree with E.R. Schweighert that the empirical evidence speaks for itself. However I would be extremely gratified if the response to this book could be a contributing factor in both the wider use of these methods by women and their sexual partners, and in the serious consideration of these ideas by Doctors and Scientists in a position to scientifically evaluate their validity and their basis.

3   ONE FERTILE TIME OR TWO?

There are still a lot of unanswered questions about how and why the lunar phase cycle works. That it is connected to and has effect on fertility is well established. But *how* it has that effect, and *what* its connection is to the hormonal cycle are not entirely clear. However there are many clues and theories which will be presented here to further understanding of this fascinating cycle.

As we have seen in Chapter 2, Dr. Jonas spent little time in examining the underlying connections between ovulation and the lunar cycle, however Dr. Rechnitz, being a gynaecologist, had this uppermost in his mind.

Rechnitz' and Jonas' figures for the distribution of conceptions between lunar and hormonal fertile times, although backed to some extent by the 30% success rate figure for the rhythm method given by Dr. Franklin Brayer, is not really corroborated by other findings, especially those relating to the use of more specific body-symptom based methods of detecting ovulation. However Rechnitz' ideas on what may be actually happening at the natal lunar phase return have provided a basis for exploration of the actual physiological events that underlie fertility at this time.

His original idea was that "increased levels of agitation" could have brought on an irregular ovulation, though he felt this could not be proved. Although it is indeed true that it has not yet been proved, we can present here a very good case for taking the idea seriously. We will also look at the possibility that the occurrence of a spontaneous ovulation at the lunar phase return is only likely if this does not coincide with the regular hormonal ovulation, and how it may be that synchronisation of these two fertility cycles may be a natural and desirable state.

If indeed the two cycles are not necessarily separate, then comparing levels of fertility on each becomes somewhat spurious. Indeed levels of fertility are extremely difficult to assess, and a woman's, or a man's, or indeed their joint fertility, may fluctuate from day to day, month to month, or year to year based on an enormous number of factors (see Chapter 6).

Over and over again in clinical use of the lunar phase cycle instances have occurred where this cycle seemingly explains otherwise puzzling phenomena. Conceptions have always been known to occur when medical models of fertility claim they are totally or nearly impossible. These times include during menstruation, during pregnancy, and on the contraceptive pill.

Many women feel sure that they know when they have conceived, only to be told by doctors that they are mistaken. Ultrasounds often give results that show the progress of the pregnancy to be 1-2 weeks at variance with the expectations of the doctor.

Many women feel sure that they know when they ovulate, have regular cycles, and yet have conceived against their wishes. These conceptions occur at times when they are quite sure that they are safe.

Doctors have traditionally felt that these instances result from the woman making a mistake of one kind or another, and doubtless many of them do. However it is also possible that a further factor in fertility, namely the lunar cycle, may be behind these seemingly "erroneous" cases.

Conception during menstruation has been explained by a combination of short cycles, long periods and the life of the sperm. As we shall see in Chapter 5, these conditions can provide a chance for conception to occur. In a short menstrual cycle ovulation may come very soon after the period. Given the presence of protective fertile mucous during the last days of menstrual bleeding, the sperm may live for several days, being unaffected by the flow of blood, and therefore reach the ovum, or egg, at ovulation. However many women conceive during their periods when they have no history of short cycles, and also are not experiencing any precipitating factors for an early ovulation such as stress, travel, medication, altered diet, ill health etc.

I have often found retrospectively that conception dates which occurred under these circumstances, or that are disputed by the Doctor, coincided with the lunar cycle.

In one such case I found that a woman's lunar return was, and had been for some time, coinciding with her period. She had been trying to conceive, but had not had sexual intercourse during her periods for religious reasons (she was Jewish). When the couple decided that conception was their first priority, and had intercourse at this time, conception occurred.

In many other cases menstruation is avoided for aesthetic reasons, or simply not used for conception attempts as it is seemingly the least likely time. It has nearly always been found to be, however, a highly fertile time if it coincides with the lunar cycle, despite the fact that the endometrium is in the least suitable state to receive the fertilised ovum. "This situation is difficult to explain" says Rechnitz.

One possible explanation would be that during the three to five days in which the fertilised egg stays in the fallopian tube, the hormonal situation, possibly changed by the spontaneous ovulation, may affect the state of the endometrium. This is, however, conjecture on my part, though a changed hormonal state induced by a spontaneous ovulation is given some credence by the observations of some of my more "experienced" clients. These women, adept at diagnosing ovulation, find that if they have sexual activity at the lunar phase recurrence, either protected through barrier methods, or for the purpose of conception, they experience known symptoms of ovulation such as sharp pains ("mittelschmirtz") and increased flow of mucous, immediately following the sex act. It is of course possible to mistake semen for mucous, and therefore controlled experiments would be needed to verify this, but most experienced users of these methods are aware of this danger, and know how to avoid it (see Chapter 5).

All users of the lunar phase cycle for cases of infertility, from Jonas onwards, agree that mid-cycle ovulation coinciding with the natal lunar phase recurrence seems to provide the optimum conditions for conception. The combination of menstruation and the lunar phase return comes a close second.

Dr. Jonas recalled, amongst many instances he had experienced of conception occurring during a "lunar" bleeding, the case of an unmarried girl who hoped to avoid pregnancy by having intercourse only during menstruation. This method failed her and she conceived. Later on, after marrying, she attempted to conceive again with no result. Jonas' calculations showed that her lunar returns and menstrual periods tended to coincide. Although "reluctant" to use this information the couple did so and conception occurred within a month.

Dr. Farsky, a Swiss doctor who uses the Lunar phase cycle to assist and prevent conception for his patients, also finds that the menstruation/lunar phase combination is often the breakthrough point in apparently infertile situations.

In the opinion of both Rechnitz and Jonas the lunar cycle may well also explain how occasionally a woman conceives a second time during her pregnancy.

"In spite of the widespread belief that during pregnancy the ovulation cycle ceases and that the woman's body contains such a large amount of pregnancy-preventing hormones that the possibility of a renewed conception is excluded, a priori, such cases do occur," they say.

To quote Jonas:- "All gynaecological magazines reported about conception during menstruation, and the first were American magazines. Further, American obstetricians were the first ones in the world to testify that a woman can conceive again even during an already existing pregnancy and that the birth connected with the first pregnancy will follow normally after nine months, and the birth of the foetus conceived afterwards will follow after a month or so, so that the time of gestation will appear as ten months."

"How this is possible no gynaecologist knows" says Jonas "because it is in contradiction of all that was stated about hormones, basal temperature and vaginal secretions."

Rechnitz and Jonas hold that the lunar cycle is responsible for these apparently impossible conceptions, and this is further backed up by the findings reported in *The Natural Birth Control Book* published by the Aquarian Research Foundation, that when a woman is using the pill in the "proper" manner then conceptions (or failures) are almost always the result of intercourse taking place at the lunar phase return.

Even if the lunar cycle can be shown to explain away all these mystery conceptions, how in fact does it work? How can conception occur in the apparent absence of ovulation? If in fact, as Rechnitz and others have suspected, there is a second, spontaneous ovulation involved, what triggers this event? And is there perhaps an underlying relationship between the lunar and hormonal cycles, spontaneous ovulation only occurring when the regular ovulation does not synchronise with this lunar time?

Let us look first at the phenomenon of spontaneous ovulation and the circumstances under which it may occur.

Certain of the smaller mammals, such as the cat and the hare do not have a fertility cycle as such. Mature follicles are always present in the ovaries of these animals, ready to burst. This happens during copulation. In an adult woman one egg is released from the ovary in mid-cycle. However there is also a capacity for this to occur at other times. According to Rechnitz "Biologically there is a possibility that tension, due to the effect of certain moon phases, builds up in the woman's nervous and hormonal systems, which in the event of sexual intercourse leads to the rupture of the follicle and thus conception. It is no accident that this connection was recognised by a psychiatrist (Jonas) and not by an obstetrician".

This activity of the ovaries is controlled by the pituitary gland which itself is influenced by the hypothalamus.

We have seen in Chapter 1 how nervous states and fertility in many animal species, including man, are influenced by moon cycles. We are also aware these days how the pituitary gland and the whole endocrine system are influenced by light. This understanding of light and its effect on humans, first pioneered by John Ott (*Health and Light*, Pocket Books, New York 1976) has been used to form the basis of "*Lunaception*", a system designed to regulate the menses by exposing the body to strong light at night (simulating the full moon).

It does not seem unreasonable to assume that a combination of the effect of light on the pituitary gland, the moon cycle on the nervous state, and the trigger effect of sexual intercourse could bring about the spontaneous release of an egg. Indeed the possibility that a spontaneous ovulation is not dependent on hormonal states as governed by the menstrual cycle is supported by the assertion that most conceptions taking place on "the pill" occur at the lunar phase return.

Spontaneous ovulation is a phenomenon long known about in medical circles, but little understood or explored. Since little has been understood about why and when it occurs it has always been a "rogue" element in fertility control. If the lunar cycle is the controlling factor, and spontaneous ovulation can occur *only* if stimulated by sexual contact and then *only* at the time of a woman's natal moon phase then we have managed to rule out one of the main difficulties in controlling fertility through its diagnosis.

If this recurring moon phase cycle works like a biological clock, a rhythm beginning at a woman's birth, becoming effective at puberty and controlling fertility through its effect on the hypothalamus, pituitary, glandular hormones and nervous states, then perhaps it has a further link, not only with the ability to spontaneously ovulate but also with the ongoing hormonal cycle.

I have found over and over again in my practice that there is a strong tendency for these two cycles to synchronise. A much higher than probable rate of synchronisation occurs in certain types of cases. Firstly in women who are trying to conceive. This tendency has been noted also by Robert Kimball's Planetary Eugenics in the 1970s. They found that the two cycles tended to synchronise in women who had been trying to conceive for at least six months, and also that conception tended to occur when this coincidence took place. They also found that in another group of women who were not trying to conceive, this pattern was not evident.

I have also found a strong tendency for synchronisation in women who are "in touch" or "in tune" with their bodies, and a marked tendency to a random relationship in women who are stressed, in poor health or have a poor body/mind relationship. Frequently women who are already using body symptom methods such as cervical mucous or basal body temperature observations, or women who simply feel that they "know" when they are ovulating come to me for the additional aspect of lunar phase charts. In an extraordinary large number of these cases we will find that the woman's cycles have been synchronising without her having any knowledge of when her lunar fertile time falls. Similarly the number of women who lead fairly rhythmic, unstressed lifestyles, notably out of urban environments and who experience lunar and hormonal fertility simultaneously, is unaccountably high.

My tentative conclusion from this evidence, which has yet to be collated and analysed on a formal and systematic basis, is that perhaps the lunar cycle is indeed a "blueprint" for our hormonal cycle, and that in a truly "natural" state we would indeed have only one fertility cycle. It seems to me that it is only when the rhythms of our life are thrown out, and our hormonal cycle is subjected to the many stresses and strains we experience daily in our modern lives, that the lunar and hormonal cycles separate. This can of course occur as the result of ill-health, chronic or acute disease states, poor nutrition, high levels of stress, excessive travel, medication, drug abuse, extreme levels of physical activity, and many other threats to our mental, emotional, psychic and physical well-being.

Many of my clients find that the very process of becoming more involved with their body states through using these methods for contraception or conception will be sufficient for the synchronisation of the two cycles to occur. Others find they have a tendency to "tune in" with other cycles in their environment, such as other women that they live or work with (this has been well documented as having such effects as causing whole dormitories of girls in boarding schools to menstruate simultaneously). They may alternatively be very aware of new and full moons and have a tendency to bleed or ovulate at one or the other. These women usually find that when their attention has been drawn to their own *personal* lunar cycle, they then are drawn towards this timing, ovulating (or sometimes menstruating) at the phase of the moon they were born at.

Yet other women find that the use of visualisations and affirmations, auto-suggestion (or self-hypnosis) techniques is useful. Just as the hormonal cycle is so obviously sensitive to all the random negative effects of various kinds of stress, so it can be programmed positively and helpfully. I encourage a programme of visualisation and affirmation to be done in a deeply relaxed or "alpha" state. Hypnosis, induced either by a therapist, with the use of a tape, or self-induced, has the same effect. These states can be induced by whatever method the woman finds acceptable and enjoyable.

She might, for example, visualise herself floating on a cloud, or rocking on some water, or merely concentrate on her breathing, directing her breath to different areas of tension. Having reached a state of deep relaxation she will then visualise herself clearly in a situation where the moon is at the same phase that she was born at. This might be, for example, three days before the full moon, and she might visualise herself looking up at a night sky with an almost full moon. She might confirm this by visualising a calendar with the days marked off to within three days of the full moon symbol. Then she would clearly visualise her reproductive system, ovaries, fallopian tubes, womb, cervix and vagina in the process of hormonal cycle ovulation. Much fertile mucous would be "seen" in the cervix and vagina to differentiate between a spontaneous and a mid-cycle ovulation (see Chapter 5). An egg would be "seen" to be released from an ovary and travel down the fallopian tube, helped along by all the little hairs inside the tube until it disintegrated (unfertilised) in the womb. This visualisation process can also be adapted to allow for personal situations and idiosyncrasies in a woman's reproductive system, like the malfunction of one ovary or tube, or conversely to encourage rather than discourage conception by taking it much further and envisaging the fertilisation of the egg, the implantation and growth into a recognisably human foetus, the development of the baby to full term and the birth process. This can then be followed by a verbal affirmation that ovulation will take place at the natal moon phase, and that conception will or will not occur.

I usually find that such activities, done regularly and with conviction, either mentally by the woman herself, or by listening to a tape that either she or I have made, or by attending sessions with myself or another therapist, will have effect in the most stubborn of cases. For those people who find such activities embarrassing, I get them to shout at themselves in the mirror with eye contact — then they really have to believe what they are saying or they feel *really* silly!

In *The Natural Birth Control Book* by the Aquarian Research Foundation they suggest that "lunaception", that is the controlling of ovulation by leaving the light on at night to simulate the full moon on 2-3 days of the cycle, and sleeping in the dark on other nights, can be used also to change the time of ovulation to coincide with the lunar return. This seems to be a useful technique for those women who have got used to responding to full moon as their time of ovulation or menstruation. In the Zambezi valley, populated for thousands of years by a stable culture, women expect to ovulate at the full moon and menstruate when the moon is new. Their houses are so constructed that there is an opening in the roof for the full moon to shine through.

There will always be those women whose cycles are so disrupted by other influences that synchronisation will not occur. Though this can often be treated by natural remedies such as herbal medicine, homoeopathy, naturopathy, osteopathy or acupuncture, there may still be some "stubborn" cases. In most instances this is not a big problem. For conception purposes synchronisation is very valuable in cases of low fertility (see Chapter 6), but for contraceptive purposes it is merely convenient. Though many women feel good at achieving synchronisation, the only real problem with not doing so if conception is *not* desired is that both fertile times need to be taken into account, thereby raising significantly the number of days in a month when abstinence or protection is required. If this is the case then again we are back to the question of spontaneous ovulation.

Masters and Johnson discovered *through laboratory observations* that "the very occasional woman ovulates out of cycle, after orgasm". What is needed now is for some research to be done to see whether these occasions occur at the return of the natal lunar phase of the woman involved. Dr. Harold Saxton Burr, working at Yale university in the late 1930s showed that 70% of the women tested sometimes ovulated outside the expected ovulation time, and the results of the work on the electronic detection of ovulation carried out by him and his student Leonard Ravitz suggest that these "extra" ovulations are often the result of intercourse.

The work of western researchers has not yet linked spontaneous ovulation with the lunar phase cycle, but there have been many connections made with electro-magnetic fields.

Burr found that each person, when tested for the strength of their body's electrical field, showed daily fluctuations, but that all the female subjects produced one huge 24 hour increase in voltage, once a month, coincident with ovulation. This he tested through the electrical field given off by the fingers. When he stimulated a female rabbit in order to produce ovulation and then opened the rabbit's abdomen and placed electrodes on the ovary itself he again found a dramatic change in voltage at the exact time of ovulation. Then an operation was carried out on a woman who had just recorded a surge on Burr's voltmeter. When her ovaries were uncovered, one contained a follicle which had just ruptured and released an egg.

Ovulation and electromagnetic fields are obviously related.

Margaret Lewis, a client of mine who works in the field of birth control and who has done her own research into possible theories behind the lunar phase cycle, points to the connection with the liquid in which the ovum is suspended. This liquid has the same salt content as the primordial sea once had when the animals climbed up onto the land. The foetus shows all the stages of evolution in its journey from egg to baby, and these beginnings in a sea-like liquid obviously provide excellent ground for the effect of electromagnetic fields.

The geomagnetic field (that of the earth) has been established as having effect on the menstrual cycle. In a survey conducted on 810 girls in a Prague nursing school, it was shown that commencement of the menstrual period is more likely during reduced geomagnetic activity, and conversely less so during increased activity. Also Birzele at Graz university in Austria established a correspondence between the duration of the period and geomagnetic disturbances. It has been shown that the greatest effect of magnetic fields on living substance consists in increasing "the reactionary speed of enzymes with corresponding effects on micro-organisms, plants and higher animals". This may have some influence on the apparently inhospitable environment that egg and sperm might find themselves in following an out of cycle ovulation.

Now if we tie these obvious connections between ovulation and electro-magnetism together with the observation that the earth's magnetic field changes slightly with the positions of the sun and moon (readings taken at Greenwich from 1916 to 1957 confirm this), we have an obvious link between ovulation, either spontaneous or mid-cycle, and the phases of the moon. Burr and his former student Leonard Ravitz found that the sun and moon influence organisms, increasing their electrical potential at new and full moons, as if there are "electric tides" in the atmosphere originating from these two bodies.

Add to this the influence of light on the endocrine system, and the fact that water, in which the ovum is suspended, is particularly susceptible to electromagnetic radiation, the trigger effects of intercourse and orgasm, and the nervous system's susceptibility to moon cycles and we have an extremely convincing case for moon cycles and ovulation cycles being inter-related.

This leaves the question of why a woman relates specifically to the phase of the moon present at her birth. Much research has gone into this question with regard to astrology generally, with a great deal of evidence being gathered by people such as Gauquelin to back up the idea of the birth time being somehow significant in terms of subsequent patterning of the individual. It has been shown that the electromagnetic fields present at conception and during the development of the embryo have a great effect upon its growth patterns (see Chapter 8). Perhaps these are the forces that influence the individual during the birth process.

All in all the picture that emerges is of a strong relationship between the menstrual cycle and the lunar cycle. One that may influence the timing of the hormonal cycle itself, based on the effects of electromagnetism and light, or one that may leave women the capacity to ovulate anyway, even though their menstrual cycle is no longer involved.

It would take little further research to verify some of these suppositions, but meanwhile we have to take note of the overwhelming experience of those who have used the lunar cycle to increase the effectiveness of their contraception programme, or their chances of conceiving. Over and over again these ideas work in practice. Therefore it would seem very foolish to ignore them!

Women seem to have very little resistance to the idea that the moon influences their fertility. It's as if for most of them this is so obvious that explanation is unnecessary. I have found that most women delight in being able to connect their personal cycles to those of the planet, in becoming aware of their interconnectedness with other living things, and in establishing their own personal relationship with the moon whilst becoming more aware of, and in tune with, their own physical changes.

However the answers are needed. Both for the satisfaction of those already using these methods, and in order to convince others so that the information can be more freely available to help the millions of women who need every little bit of help they can get to feel in control of their own fertility.

4   MEN TOO

It takes two to tango — and it takes two (the number allocated numerologically to the moon!) to perform the dance of creativity. Babies have fathers too! and those paternal instincts (if they have motivated any men to read this book) may well by now be feeling a little neglected. This is where we rectify that. The reason men seem to have such a small slice of attention in this book is simple, and springs from purely practical reasons.

Male fertility behaves differently from female fertility. Most men, who have a healthy and viable sperm count and good sperm mobility and motility, are fertile *all the time*. And therefore there is very little need to study the patterns of their fertility. We simply know that although the woman's fertility may determine whether or not a certain sexual act is likely to result in conception, the man's is not usually a factor that needs to be considered. I say "usually" because there are cases where it can be an important consideration. Those men whose sperm count is low, or who have poor sperm mobility or motility, may need to know how to take advantage of their own fertility patterns, if they wish to have children.

Men have a lunar cycle too.

I have heard the theory put forward that a man's continual fertility is the reason for his supposedly more constant and vigorous sexual appetite, whereas a woman's cyclical fertility may account for her more "selective" sexual nature.

Although I would dispute (hotly!) the assumption that men's sexuality is more lusty than a woman's, obviously each sex has differences in the expression of that sexuality, and perhaps there is some truth that women, in general, appear to be more discriminating in their sexual behaviour. It is certainly true that the intensity of their sexuality, as their fertility, is cyclical in nature.

The link between sexuality and fertility is demonstrated also by the role that frequency of sexual activity seems to play in the speed with which fertility returns after childbirth. During breastfeeding (without which of course, in the absence of disease, fertility returns immediately) one of the factors which hastens the return of the menstrual cycle is a full and active sex life.

Interestingly enough, many women feel relatively sexually uninterested during this period, and perhaps this is also part of Mother Nature's way of spacing children. If so, then indeed this is the only breathing space most women are accorded by Her, as if we truly followed Nature's plan, and "tuned in" to our cycles in the fullest sense, then reproduction would occur on most possible occasions. Reproduction is, after all, what nature is about. The majority of women feel most highly sexually motivated when they are ovulating, and also, as is reported to me by my clients, during their lunar fertility. The highly sexual feelings experienced by some women just before and during menstruation might seem to contradict this, but is in fact due to a "mixed message". As the womb distends with blood it can be interpreted by the body as part of the experience of orgasm, when this also occurs.

However if fertility is indeed an underlying sexual motivation, we can also expect a man's sexual nature to vary quite rhythmically.

As we shall see, although a man's fertility is generally adequate for fertilization to occur at all times, the sperm count does indeed respond to a lunar cycle, and peaks quite markedly when the moon is at the same angle to the sun as it was at the man's birth. This information is not of particular importance if conception is being avoided, as most men still have a viable number of healthy sperm even when "off-peak"! But it becomes crucial if low sperm count is part of a couple's infertility problem.

I first heard reports of research into a lunar cycle for men many years ago when I was beginning to make lunar charts for my female clients. I heard that in Britain there had been research showing that sperm count went as high as ten times "normal" levels at the man's natal lunar phase. (I believe that some research has also been done into astrobiological calculations of male fertility by Joseph Kosichek in Toronto, who is mentioned by Lynn Schroeder and Sheila Ostrander in their book *Astrological Birth Control*.)

Although I could not find the source of this information I decided to try it out. Some helpful male clients co-operated and had sperm count tests done at both "peak" and "off-peak" lunar times. The reports were very encouraging, although the sample was small. One man found that his normal level being 1.8 million, which is very low, his peak reading was up to 52 million, which is quite adequate for fertilization to occur. These results, though too small to provide proof, seem to indicate that it is indeed worth taking the man's lunar cycle into account when working with male fertility problems.

When a couple are attempting to deal with infertility, the first line of approach is to find out whether there is a low sperm count or lack of sperm mobility/motility. This is firstly because the test, although perhaps a little embarrassing, is not surgically intrusive or painful, and has no possible side effects, unlike the majority of tests that can be performed on the woman. Also the results (allowing for period fluctuation) are clear and definite. Either there is a problem, or there isn't. Woman's fertility is much more complex, and targeting the problem, or being sure there isn't one, is a much more difficult procedure.

Let's just define the terms count, mobility and motility. "Mobility" refers to the ability of the sperm to propel themselves, "motility" to the number of sperm still active after a few hours, and "sperm count" to the number of sperm in a given amount of seminal fluid. "Normal" range is considered 30-60 million sperm per millilitre. This may seem like an enormous number when only one is needed to fertilise the egg, but the sperm have to face many hazards on their journey!

Firstly, many get killed by the acidity in the vagina before they reach the "safety" of the alkaline cervix (acidity is inimical to sperm). Then many get "lost" in the uterus, simply swimming around and around until they die, never finding the two exits to the fallopian tubes, in one of which the egg is waiting. Then many which do find one of the tube entrances will choose the wrong one! An egg is normally only released by one ovary in each cycle, usually alternately. So what starts off like the crowd in the "City to Surf" marathon thins down just as rapidly!

If there is a low sperm count or a lack of mobility or motility the treatment is also, like the test, fairly straightforward. In my practice I use herbal medicine, combined with an appraisal of diet, vitamin and mineral supplementation, and other factors. Other practitioners might treat with acupuncture, or homoeopathy. Vitamin C has been shown to be especially important for sperm motility. Unfortunately one cannot rely on fresh fruit for one's intake of this, or any other, vitamin.

Although ideally our food is the best way to receive our vitamins and minerals, tests show that the apparently fresh fruit in our greengrocers are often sadly lacking in essential nutrients. One orange when tested may show an adequate level of vitamin C, and another virtually none at all. Prolonged shelf life, often artificially extended, combined with sprays and chemical fertilizers, seem to have robbed our fruit and vegetables of their capacity to be a reliable source of nutrients. In order to maintain adequate levels of vitamin C therefore, daily supplementation is necessary.

Other vitamins important for male fertility are B12 and E, and zinc is an essential mineral. Smoking is extremely detrimental, especially since it lowers levels of these nutrients. Diet is of course important, even though supplementation may also be necessary, and plenty of fresh fruit and vegetables, especialy watercress, which has "goodies" galore, should be combined with an adequate protein source. If meat is not eaten, fish is a wonderful protein-rich food happily lacking saturated fats. Vegetarians must be careful, as many are not, to ensure protein levels are high enough without overdosng on dairy products (high in saturated fats). However anyone with a severe fertility problem should consult a naturopath or nutritionist as each case is decidedly unique, and these are very general guidelines.

Ginseng has long been associated with high male fertility levels, and Bee Pollen also has a good reputation. Octocosanal, a substance found in wheat germ oil (also high in vitamin E), can be useful too.

Herbal medicines are very powerful in raising sperm count and restoring mobility and motility. These should be dispensed by a practising medical herbalist, allowing for the particular situation, and will take into account the health of the individual. My own general formula, which is of course only a basis, and is often changed to allow for specific health considerations, is as follows:

Fluid Extract Oats	0.5 mL
Fluid Extract Sarsaparilla	8.0 mL
Fluid Extract Black Willow	1.0 mL
Fluid Extract Saw Palmetto	0.5 mL
Fluid Extract Damiana	2.0 mL

This makes a full dose of 12 mL. Owing to the "potentiating" effect of the herbs on each other, half of this, 6 mL, is a sufficient dose, which should be taken, at the discretion of the herbalist, three time daily in a little water.

Expect an increased growth of facial hair, renewed vigour and heightened sexual appetite!

Since pressure and heat destroy sperm, hot baths and tight pants should be avoided. I have known one case of male infertility caused by frequent wearing of a wet-suit!

Once the lunar cycle has been calculated for the male partner, showing the times each month when the sun-moon angle is the same as at his birth, and thus when his fertility peaks, we are then left with another problem to solve. The female partner may not be fertile at this time. Now with the woman fertility is either there or not, unlike the "peaking" effect with the man, and it's obviously no use having a high level of male fertility if the woman is simply infertile on those days.

The woman's lunar fertility is unlikely to coincide with the man's, though of course in some fortunate cases this may occur. Only those partners who are born at approximately the same time in the lunar month can both expect to be fertile on the lunar cycle at the same time. This leaves the option of synchronising the woman's hormonal cycle ovulation with the male partner's fertility peak.

As we have discussed in Chapter 3, it is quite possible to synchronise the woman's lunar and hormonal cycles, using auto-suggestion techniques. In cases where low sperm count is the prime consideration it may be advisable to use this process to bring the mid-cycle ovulation in line with the male partner's lunar fertility time, instead of with the woman's. All that is required is to replace the woman's natal phase in the suggestion with the man's. The man might want to join in the visualisation and affirmation process, and create for himself the image of plentiful sperm, programming his own body into healthful fertility. As a last resort, it is even possible to take sperm from the man at his lunar fertility peak, and artificially inseminate into the woman at hers.

Sperm count checks can be carried out at regular intervals to check progress, without any risk to the man. It is necessary to know at which point in the male lunar cycle the check is carried out, to know whether it is the "peak" or "trough" level which is being measured. In this way we can see the difference between these two readings, and also monitor progress being made with medication (such as herbal extracts).

When normal levels are achieved, then conception should occur. If it does then it is time to consider whether there are factors in the woman's fertility which are affecting the issue. We will look further at these in Chapter 6. It is also possible for the problem to be mutual, in that some women develop resistence, or antibodies, to their partner's sperm, or may have mucous which is hostile.

Whatever the diagnosis of fertility problems, both partners will need to be supportive of each other. Stress has an enormously detrimental effect on both male and female fertility. Babies born into loving relationships not only have a better life — they are more likely to have a life at all!

5   CONTRACEPTION

Surprisingly large numbers of otherwise health conscious women are consuming each day, along with their vitamins and minerals, another pill which even orthodox medical practitioners have become dubious about, the contraceptive pill. Sold on the idea that so called "freedom" of sexual expression is a necessary part of modern-day life and relationships, these people endanger their mental and physical health in this cause in ways that they would never consider for any other reason. Women are afraid of their partners being "put off" by an open admittance of the fact that sexual intercourse and reproduction are two facets of the same biological function. Women have been encouraged to abuse their bodies so that men can have untrammelled access to them at all times, and men have been encouraged to completely ignore any responsibility they might have towards prevention of conception.

I feel that this "freedom" is in fact quite the opposite, and that these attitudes are not only unrealistic, but can cause resentment, alienation, frigidity and generally chauvinist and uncaring relationships, as well as putting undue strain on the woman's health.

Sexuality is the tool of reproduction. This does not necessarily imply, as is claimed by some extremists, that sexual expression of love for another adult is wrong if not carried out for the express purpose of conception, but it does mean that the two are irrevocably linked, and that any attempt to pretend otherwise will only confuse our efforts towards self-awareness and bringing our bodies and minds into greater harmony.

The emphasis in natural birth control methods is on encouraging the woman into further involvement with and understanding of her reproductive functions, rather than attempting to disguise them.

Many women, having heard continually of the notorious "rhythm" method, the jokes about large Catholic families and most people's opinions about the hit-and-miss and unreliable affair that natural methods used to be, have left the subject unexplored and have turned, in some cases reluctantly, to the more orthodox methods. However natural methods today are updated and precise and when used correctly are 98-99% effective.

So if you are a woman who desires to interfere with her body functions as little as possible, and at the same time retain control over her own fertility, or if you merely have a problem finding a suitable and reliable method of birth control, then you will be pleased to hear that there is a real alternative.

The number of women who are dissatisfied with orthodox contraception methods is steadily increasing as the dangers of the pill are more fully recognised and fewer women feel happy about putting up with the pain and chances of infection so often present with I.U.Ds. Many women are turning to spermicide foams, diaphragms and condoms, but, as these are often inconvenient and messy, they often do not provide a satisfactory full-time alternative.

Natural methods are both reliable and effective when used by women who are sufficiently motivated to bring some concentration and determination to bear in their use of them. Women can be taught how to know when they are fertile, and given guidelines as to what measures to take when this is so. In order for a woman to embark on using natural contraception she needs to have a healthy and curious attitude towards her own body and its functions, a determination to persevere in her attempts to learn more about them and hopefully a co-operative sexual partner.

They not only offer a reasonable, safe and effective alternative, but have several other advantages.

Firstly there is no reliance on manufactured goods or specialist knowledge. These methods can be utilised effectively in whatever circumstances a woman finds herself, and will continue to be appropriate through all aspects of fertile life, including trying to conceive, breast-feeding and the sometimes chaotic approach to menopause. Although it is helpful initially to consult with a teacher or therapist who can advise on the particular case and ensure that the methods are fully understood, and to have the teacher there as back-up in cases of difficulty, after the initial consultations the woman (or couple) is self-sufficient. There is no more necessity for visits to chemists' shops, medical or prescription fees. These methods are applicable for all women, whether their cycle is regular or not. Once the signs of fertility have been understood, then they can be recognised whether they come regularly once a month, or in an entirely sporadic fashion.

Secondly there are no harmful chemicals or uncomfortable devices involved and therefore no side effects. Later we will look at the problems associated with the more "orthodox" methods of contraception.

Thirdly these methods encourage a woman to a more intimate knowledge of her own body and its functions. This can reward both curiosity and the harmonious interaction between a woman's physical and emotional states. It can bring a whole new dimension of awareness to sexual activity and often helps remove sexual blocks caused by ignorance and fear.

Fourthly it becomes possible for the male partner to share more actively in the responsibility of fertility control. The woman usually feels intense relief at no longer being the one to shoulder all the responsibility for birth control, and also because she is no longer risking her health for the sake of the relationship. Most men are also pleased to be able to take a more active and responsible role, and to reduce the health burden on their partners. Of course, if a woman is not in a regular relationship, or has an unco-operative partner, it is still quite possible for her to assume control of the situation, and use these methods successfully.

Fifthly if conception *is* desired these methods can help couples who are having difficulty conceiving or maintaining a healthy pregnancy (see Chapter 6).

Sixthly, this is the only form of contraception which doesn't employ "overkill" methods. All other methods guard against conception 100% of the time, whereas in fact a woman is naturally infertile for the majority of her cycle and has no need of contraception except for a few days each month.

Lastly if an unwanted pregnancy should result, and the chance of this happening using these methods is about as low as that offered by any other, there will be no complications to the pregnancy caused by the method of contraception.

One thing can be certain using natural methods — the only complication can be pregnancy, and the chances of this occurring are as slight as with any other available method.

The Bad News — Problems of "Orthodox" Methods
Let us look further at some of the problems attached to "orthodox" methods of contraception.

The Pill
The pill is by now notorious for its drawbacks, dangers and side effects. The so-called "minor" disadvantages include such effects as weight gain, acne, skin discoloration, migraines, vaginal discharges including a much greater tendency to vaginal thrush (yeast infection), urinary tract infections, eye disorders such as double vision, swelling of the optic nerve, contact lens intolerance and corneal inflammation, varicose veins, disturbances in liver function, commonly associated with allergic reactions such as increased incidence of rhinitis, hay fever, asthma and skin rashes, decreased immune response, eczema, mouth ulcers, cervical erosions, hair loss or facial and body hair growth, and a huge range of psychological and emotional disorders, usually labelled "Depression". This includes sexual depression or loss of libido (sex drive) which is jokingly referred to as the way the pill works!

Now these "minor" side effects, though not life threatening, can obviously be extremely distressing if they occur to any great extent, and many women coming off the pill, in my experience, report a much greater feeling of "well-being", often unrelated to specific conditions, and often only realised after the effects of the pill have worn off (a process which can take some months). Indeed a 10 year programme by the Californian Walnut Creek drug study of hospitals admissions reports significantly increased inflammatory diseases in women under 40 who have taken or currently take "the pill". These inflammatory conditions include respiratory, digestive, urogenital and musculoskeletal disorders.

Then of course there are the "high level" risks such as a greatly increased chance of suffering a stroke, increased risk of blood clots, of gall bladder diseases, disturbances to blood sugar metabolism which can lead to diabetes or hypoglycemia, liver tumours, an increased chance of hardening of the arteries and high blood pressure, a 3-6 fold increased risk of heart attacks, according to age, a significantly higher risk of developing breast cancer, and the strong probability of any pre-existing cancers developing much more rapidly.

Many of these side-effects are a direct result of the fact that whilst a woman is on the pill she is deficient in a large number of nutrients. Conversely some of the effects of the pill themselves cause further deficiencies. Ingestion of the pill creates a false state of pregnancy, placing the woman's body in a continuous state of preparation for the (non-existent) developing foetus.

Vitamin A levels in the blood are increased on the pill. Whether this means that the body's turnover of this vitamin is higher (requiring a higher level of ingestion) as there is less stored in the liver, or whether in fact there is a greater availability to the tissues is not yet clear.

Vitamin B1 is probably deficient in pill-takers. Side effects include fatigue, weight loss, depression, irritability, oversensitivity to noise, loss of appetite and circulatory problems.

Vitamin B2 requirements of the body are raised by use of the pill, leading to deficiencies. Side effects include gum and mouth infections, eye irritation, skin problems and dandruff.

Vitamin B6 depletion varies from marginal to severe. Side effects include low stress tolerance, lethargy, depression, weakness, and nervousness.

Folic acid levels are reduced on the pill. The most severe problem resulting from this is if conception occurs during pill use or in the period following, when the body is still recovering. Since folic acid is required by the body to facilitate cell division, a process that starts immediately after conception, there is a much higher risk of birth defects if this vitamin is deficient.

Vitamin B12 levels in the blood are lowered in pill users. Resulting effects include anaemia, weight loss and depression.

Vitamin C levels are reduced, and this is worsened by smoking, stress, high pollution levels and some medications. This can result in bruising, bleeding gums and fatigue.

Vitamin E is decreased. Effects include anaemia, muscle degeneration and hot flushes.

Vitamin K levels are increased. Vitamin K increases blood clot formation.

Calcium absorption is improved.

Copper absorption is increased, raising the body's need for Vitamin C.

Zinc levels are significantly lowered on the pill. This can lead to diabetes, poor resistance to infection, skin infections, lowered fertility, and many other problems.

Blood lipids, specifically Low Density Lipids and Tryglycerides (the baddies) are increased on the pill, increasing the chances of heart disease.

Once a woman decides to stop taking the pill and start a family, she may find that she is suffering from the most ironic and perhaps distressing side effect of all, infertility.

Sometimes the body has difficulty readjusting to the fact that ovulation is no longer suppressed and the menstrual cycle does not recommence satisfactorily, with either a lack of menstruation, ovulation, or sufficient mucous production resulting. This can be a temporary or permanent condition, which happily often responds to natural remedies.

The I.U.D.

The I.U.D. (Inter-uterine device) is actually physically rejected by a great many women, and those who can tolerate it are prone to the so-called minor side effects of heavy periods and cramping, sometimes with severe pain. This may be due to the abortive effect of the I.U.D., which is not strictly a contraceptive, and allows conception to occur, subsequently causing an abortion by preventing the fertilised egg's attachment to the wall of the womb. The fact that the I.U.D. is in fact an abortificant is often not known by the user, and its discovery can cause moral, ethical or religious distress.

The heavy bleeding and cramps, and indeed the egg's inability to attach to the uterine wall, are both also due to the constant inflammation and irritation that the I.U.D. sets up in the uterine tissue. This is in itself a cause for concern, particularly with those women who are becoming more sensitive to subtle body energy flows.

However the more serious problem is the high incidence of pelvic inflammatory disease, (P.I.D.). It is believed that the bacteria causing the infection may travel up the cord hanging from the I.U.D. in the usually sterile uterus into the non-sterile vagina. These infections are usually fairly well progressed before much pain is felt, and therefore are often not diagnosed until they have progressed up to the fallopian tubes, where they may cause adhesions and scarring, blocking the tubes and leavng the woman infertile. If the infection is severe, a Hysterectomy can be advised (and may even be necessary! — although it is the most frequently performed unnecessary operation in the

Western world). If the ovaries are also removed this can result in an unnaturally early menopause which is often then treated with synthetic oestrogen.

I.U.D.s can also become lodged in the wall of the uterus, and may perforate it. Diabetic women have been found to have a 37% failure rate with copper I.U.D.s resulting from the negating effect of their excessive metabolic production of sulphur and chloride, which accumulate on the device. Unfortunately if the device fails as a contraceptive the resulting pregnancy may be problematic (see next section).

Barrier Methods

Barrier methods such as diaphragms and condoms have less problems associated with their use, and are becoming a lot more popular, though many couples find that their continued use has difficulties. They can cause embarrassment, are messy, and interfere with spontaneity of expression and tactile experience in foreplay and intercourse. Also many women (and men) are allergic to, or wary of, the spermicides which are often used in conjunction with these methods.

However some women combine limited use of the barrier methods with the knowledge of their fertile times, as they find several days of abstinence too difficult. This cuts down on their use of the devices to a few days in each cycle, and we shall talk about how to combine this approach with fertility diagnostic techniques later in this chapter.

Problem Pregnancies

The other dangers with orthodox methods of contraception are the complications caused to the pregnancy should one occur in spite of the measures taken to prevent it.

Pills prescribed these days are usually very low dosage (thankfully), but this means that they have to be taken with great regularity to be effective, preferably at the same time each day. Consequently more women are conceiving whilst on the pill, and may continue to take it into the first few months of pregnancy, thus severely altering the climate that the foetus grows in. Deficiencies of Folic Acid, for example, have been linked with an up to five times greater chance of giving birth to a child with limb defects, and with the incidence of Down's syndrome, or Mongolism. There is also a much higher incidence of still-births, miscarriages, and birth defects in children conceived within a month of coming off the pill.

The hormones from the pill are not effectively eliminated by the body for up to 5 months after its use is discontinued. Therefore any pregnancy initiated within that time may be affected.

I.U.D.s have been known to lodge in the foetus (luckily not too many cases are recorded) and, more commonly, cause the fertilised egg to attach in the fallopian tubes instead of in the womb (which is too inflamed by the device). These ectopic pregnancies are highly dangerous, sometimes fatal, requiring immediate surgery. A conception that occurs in the presence of an I.U.D. is also much more likely to result in a septic abortion.

Barrier methods present no threat of their own, but there is speculation that spermicides may cause birth defects by damaging instead of killing the sperm on its way to fertilise the egg. This is luckily fairly improbable as defective sperm are unlikely to be the winners in this highly competitive race! There is, however, evidence that they can affect the foetus adversely, causing deformities, if used into the early months of pregnancy.

With natural methods if an unwanted pregnancy does occur, and the chances of this are about as slight as with any other method (provided, as with any methods, that they are applied correctly), at least there is no threat to the pregnancy from the contraceptive method employed.

There can be no side effects with natural methods, as the body is not affected in any way. The woman is learning to work with the body's natural rhythms, rather than trying to control, suppress or alter them.

Informed Use of "Artificial" Methods
Don't despair if you feel that there is a need for you to use one of these artificial contraception approaches. Certainly there are times in many women's lives when they may choose to do so for a number of reasons. Most often the problems arise when neither the woman nor her physician are careful enough to check past personal and family history, and monitor ongoing use of these methods. Of course the most careful checking cannot eliminate all the risks, but forewarned is forearmed. The important thing is for a woman to make an *informed* choice and not blindly follow the advice of a less than thorough medical practitioner as is unfortunately too often the case.

Certainly natural methods are not suitable for all people all of the time and can really only be used effectively by those who are motivated to do so.

That's enough words on the negative aspects of devices and chemicals — now for the good news!

The Good News
Natural methods of contraception, relying on diagnosis of the fertile days in each cycle, are applicable to all stages of a woman's fertile life. Once a woman has learnt to distinguish fertility she can continue to do so effectively during irregular

cycles and even in the sometimes confusing times after childbirth and approaching menopause. The only limiting factor for its use is the motivation of the woman and her partner. It should only be considered by those who are prepared to use the method whole-heartedly and who are willing to commit their time and attention especially during the first few months as they learn what is involved and establish new habits.

Quite soon these new patterns become automatic, and the processes become really very simple, as much a part of the woman's life as cleaning her teeth. In fact once a woman is aware of her fertility it's usually something she can't imagine ever having not known, it becomes as much a part of her body awareness as whether she has a cold or a headache!

Awareness of the lunar phase fertile time (usually charted by a therapist, Natural birth control counsellor or an astrologer) must of course be used in conjunction with diagnosis of mid-cycle ovulation. There are three methods commonly used for this, rhythm method (calculations), ovulation method (cervical mucous testing) and temperature readings. These last two are often combined and called the sympto-thermal method.

When Jonas was doing his original research the sympto-thermal approach was not in use, and he and Dr. Rechnitz combined the lunar phase awareness with the rhythm method. Although they had great success, there are many advantages to using the sympto-thermal approach, and these days Rhythm has really been relegated to a back seat. However it still has a part to play as we shall see.

Lunar Cycle

Let us look first at how the lunar cycle can be used for contraception.

As we have seen, the fertile time for a woman on this cycle, whether or not it coincides with the mid-cycle ovulation, occurs at the repetition of the angle between the sun and the moon, as seen from the earth, at the time of her birth.

Let us suppose that Ms XYZ was born when the sun moon angle was 60°. This occurs about 5 days after the new moon. She will then be fertile according to Jonas' findings 5 days after each new moon and for a period either side of this peak time. To calculate the natal angle (in this case 60°) the time, date and place of birth need to be reasonably accurately known. As the sun/moon angle increases by approximately one degree every two hours, the information on time of birth does not need to be as accurately known as for, say, a horoscope, where the degree of the ascendant (the sign of the zodiac rising over the horizon at the time of birth) can change every 4 minutes. Birth time is valid even if birth was induced, or performed by caesarean section. If the birth took place in a hospital these records are usually still available, although sometimes if the hospital has closed down or changed its function its records may need tracking down, and occasionally may have been lost or destroyed. Most mothers can remember at least an approximate birth time, (for example "early morning" is better than nothing) and in the absence of any accurate informaton, a noon time is taken and safety margins added to allow for error.

Having established a reasonably accurate time, date and place of birth, astronomical tables can be consulted to give the natal angle, or the angle between the sun and moon present at birth. The recurrence of this angle once every lunar month can then be accurately predicted using the same astronomical tables.

A more detailed explanation of how the lunar cycle calculations are made, and their relationship to the appearance of the moon in the sky can be found in Chapter 10.

Once we know when, each month, the woman is experiencing her peak potential fertility on the lunar cycle (at the *exact* recurrence of the natal angle), we then add safety margins for possible error, egg and sperm life. This results in a 4 day interval, constructed thus:-

4-DAY LUNAR FERTILE INTERVAL

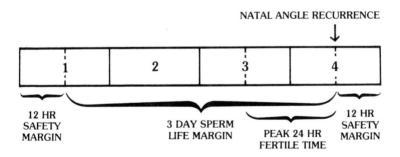

The reasons for the safety margins are explained fully in Chapter 10.

This 4-day interval will recur once per lunar month, or approximately every twenty nine and a half days, 12-13 times a year, and remains potentially fertile wherever it falls in the menstrual cycle, with fertility enhanced by its coincidence with either menstruation or, to a greater extent, with mid-cycle ovulation.

Though the lunar phase fertile times are predictable, fixed and unaffected by the woman's health or the timing of her ovulation cycle (in fact the moon would need to be blown off course for them to change!) the reverse may not be true. As we saw in Chapter 3 the ovulation cycle is often affected by the lunar cycle and may well synchronise with it given a lack of disturbing stimuli.

Although it may be true that the lunar cycle is a rhythmic blueprint for the ovulation cycle, any number of factors can throw the hormonal cycle "off-course". These include ill-health, diet changes, weight changes, excessive exercise, drug taking (prescription or otherwise), travel, stress, trauma or any other disturbance in the normal rhythmic flow of a woman's mental, emotional and physical well-being. If the two cycles do not coincide there will be *two fertile times a month* to be taken into consideration when sexual activity must either be protected or avoided. Synchronisation of the lunar and hormonal cycles, though useful and perhaps indicative of harmony, is by no means essential. There is no need to feel concerned if it does not occur.

If the lunar and mid-cycle fertile times do not coincide, the lunar fertility remains *potential* only. Sexual activity at this time may trigger the release of an egg spontaneously, or it may not. Whether or not spontaneous ovulation does occur, there will be no build-up of warning signs in the body, as there is at mid-cycle ovulation. Although clients of mine, used to detecting ovulation, have reported many signs of ovulation occurring at this time if sexual activity does occur, these will not precede the "trigger" event.

Much research is needed to see how, if a spontaneous ovulation is triggered, this affects other physiological states, such as the condition of the mucous and the endometrium (lining of the womb). Reports I have gathered (though as yet I have done no systematic research) indicate a sudden change in the mucous, accompanied by ovulation pains. However it is important to realise that you cannot rely on these changes to diagnose fertility at this time. It would certainly seem essential for these changes to occur in order for the prevailing conditions to favour conception, but as far as contraception at the lunar return is concerned, abstinence (in order not to trigger an ovulation) or precautions (in case this does occur) are essential.

So to use the lunar phase cycle for contraceptive purposes, all that is essential is that the woman is aware of when the fertile times will be (a therapist or astrologer will chart these in advance) and then avoid unprotected intercourse at these times.

Menstrual/Ovulation Hormonal Cycle

Let us now look at the methods that are available for diagnosing fertility on the hormonal cycle.

The fertile times on this cycle have to be assessed by the individual woman from cycle to cycle, as timing can be affected by stress, ill health, travel, diet and weight changes, drug taking (prescription or otherwise) or any drastic change in circumstances. The likely effects of these factors will vary from woman to woman, and will of course be much more accurately assessed as the woman becomes more familiar with her cycle.

There are basically two ways of telling when ovulation occurs, by calculation (rhythm method) or by observation of body symptoms such as changes in cervical mucous and body-at-rest temperature that occur at different stages of the cycle (sympto-thermal method). Observation has the obvious advantages of being more accurate, and therefore requiring less abstinence or occasions when protection is required. Observation methods also encourage involvement in, and awareness of, the reproductive functions, bringing greater accuracy, and more likelihood of the two cycles coinciding.

The best course of action is to rely on the sympto-thermal method whenever possible, and to use rhythm method as back-up, fail-safe, and as a warning of when ovulation is likely to be due.

There are teachers of natural methods who claim that a mix-and-match approach is confusing, and that a woman should stick to one method. I have not found this to be the case, nor have other researchers. Different methods give slightly different information and can therefore complement each other. One method may be ruled out by some circumstances, and it is useful to have other ways of determining fertility. I have usually found that a woman is happy to have as much information as possible at her fingertips so she can use the method(s) most appropriate for her, in whatever circumstances she finds herself. If we can avoid making too many rules, and offer as many options as possible, the methods remain flexible, and appropriate in conditions which might otherwise be difficult. Information is much more useful than rules and a woman is not left without guidelines when her circumstances vary from the norm.

For example if a woman generally relies on mucous observations to tell when she is ovulating, and suddenly finds herself suffering from an acute yeast infection, with a large amount of discharge (easily brought on by warm weather, tight trousers or synthetic underwear), she can, if familiar with either rhythm or temperature methods, use these until she has treated the condition (4 drops of Tea-tree oil and 2 tablespoons of cider vinegar in 2 litres of warm water make a very effective douche). Similarly a sudden bout of frequent love making could compromise mucous observations, or the pattern might change dramatically from her normal experience, and she might feel insecure about her interpretation. Although mucous observations tell us that a woman's body is preparing to ovulate, only temperature readings (or a blood test) can confirm that this has taken place, and having used temperature readings for some months information as to the normal length of the second half of a woman's cycle can help her to make a more accurate rhythm calculation.

In this way a woman can use one or all of these methods alone or in combination to diagnose ovulation under almost any circumstances.

Rhythm Method

In the rhythm method a woman calculates, based on her previous experiences and the recent history of her cycle, when she *thinks* she is likely to ovulate. Having this information marked in, in advance, means that if there is any lack of confidence in interpretation of signs of fertility, rhythm method can be resorted to for that month, and the fertile period is unlikely to be passed without the woman being alerted to the possibility that she has become fertile without noticing it.

Rhythm method also provides helpful backup while mucous patterns are initially being learnt, and the woman is still not sufficiently familiar with her body changes.

The main disadvantages of rhythm, as opposed to the sympto-thermal method, are firstly that it doesn't account for unpredictable changes in the cycle, and secondly that even when working fairly reliably, its effectiveness does rely on fairly large safety margins and will always involve more abstinence than the sympto-thermal approach. However, for a fairly regular woman, as long as it's combined with the Lunar Phase cycle observance, it can provide, as we saw from Dr. Jonas' research, reliable contraception.

Rhythm Formulas

There are two different formulas for rhythm calculations. There's one which can be found in most publications which is very cautious and gives protection for the fertile days associated with any possible repetition of the longest and shortest cycles experienced over the last year.

This formula is to subtract 19 days from the shortest recorded cycle, to give the possible beginning of fertility, and 10 days from the longest recorded cycle to give the end of the fertile period.

S—19 to L—10

For example a shortest recorded cycle of 26 days gives day 7 as the beginning of the possibly fertile period, and a longest recorded cycle of 34 gives day 24 as the end. Day 1 of a cycle is always taken as the first day of actual flow of blood (spotting does not count). This calculation relies on several assumptions.

Firstly it assumes that the second half of the cycle (from ovulation to menstruation) is approximately 14 days long. Now for the average woman this may be so. After the ovary has released an egg it takes approximately two weeks for the follicle to heal, and menstruation to begin. However, the luteal phase, as this second half of the cycle is called, can vary quite a lot from the standard 14 days. Some women have a regularly shorter second half and some regularly longer. Other women may find that it varies slightly, and some women have one ovary that behaves differently from the other, giving rise to alternating cycle lengths (ovaries usually take it in turns to ovulate). The useful thing about using a Mix-and-Match approach is that temperature readings can confirm the body's usual pattern and this personal information can then be used in the formula instead of the average expectation of 14.

The second assumption is that the cycle will continue to behave as it has done in the recent past. Given an increasing awareness of how different circumstances affect the cycle, this information can be taken into consideration. The longest cycle in the last year's records may have coincided with a particular set of circumstances which the woman knows tends to lengthen her cycle, but which no longer prevail. Or the whole pattern may have changed drastically and records as far in the past as a year ago might be considered irrelevant.

I feel that with an increased awareness of an individual cycle, the formula can be adapted to the particular situation without loss of safety, given that the woman is careful in her interpretation.

The formula could then be seen as follows.

1. Take the shortest cycle length experienced in the last year (excluding freak cycles from known causes, as long as these no longer prevail).

2. Subtract the longest likely duration of the second half of the cycle (possibly around 14 but maybe longer).

3. Subtract 3 more days for the lifespan of the sperm (sperm can live up to 3 days in fertile mucous).

This gives the first day of the possibly fertile period.

Then for the last day:

1. Take the longest cycle length experienced in the last year (excluding freak cycles from known causes as long as these no longer prevail).

2. Subtract the shortest likely duration of the second half of the cycle (possibly around 14 but maybe shorter).

3. Add one more day to account for the life span of the egg (usually only 12 hours but possibly up to 24).

This gives the last day of the possibly fertile period.

These safety margins can be increased if there is any reason to suppose that present conditions may lengthen or shorten the cycle. Rhythm calculations cannot be relied upon in very unstable situations. Experience will tell what these are for each individual, and until such information is available, stress, travel, drugs (prescription or not), weight and diet changes, ill health, and any major change in emotional or physical conditions must be considered suspect.

Long and Short Cycles

In cycles that are longer or shorter than average, given that the second half of the cycle remains fairly stable (and this is nearly always the case), the first half will be where the expansion or contraction takes place. Thus a long cycle is nearly always due to a delayed ovulation, not an overdue period, and a short cycle to an early ovulation.

AVERAGE 29 DAY CYCLE

LONG 36 DAY CYCLE

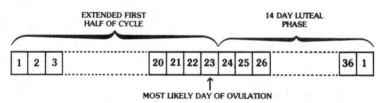

SHORT 24 DAY CYCLE

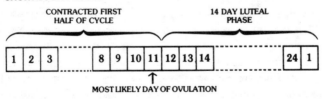

Sometimes an abnormally long or short luteal phase is due to a hormonal imbalance and can be corrected with natural therapies, for example with hormonally balancing herbs such as Chastetree and True or False Unicorn Root, though for some women it seems to be natural to their cycle. In the section on the temperature method we will discuss how this can be evaluated.

Until there is verification from the temperature readings over several cycles of the normal length of the luteal phase, 14 days can be taken as a fairly accurate guess, with the usual variation being from 12 to 16. Under these conditions the formula "S-19 to L-10" is best used.

In a very short cycle, if the length of the luteal phase is fairly normal, ovulation can come very soon after the menstrual period. This may mean that the fertile mucous which precedes ovulation, and enables the sperm to survive, may well be present during bleeding. The flow of blood is not sufficient to expel either the mucous or the sperm, and therefore the period can be potentially fertile (the only other time that this can occur is if it coincides with the lunar fertile time, and spontaneous ovulation occurs).

This is another reason to use the rhythm calculation as back-up, as it can warn of this possibility, whereas mucous detection may be impossible while blood is present. Women with regularly long cycles will probably not need to allow for this possibility, but those who have occasional or frequent short cycles should be very careful, and in very unstable situations it is probably safer for anyone to consider the menstrual period as possibly fertile.

Rhythm calculations, though useful as back-up, should *never* be followed if they contradict body symptoms. Body symptoms *always* take precedence over calculations, as they tell what's *really* going on.

Mucous Observations

The most important body symptom to be observed is the change in the cervical mucous. This is because it's the one observable change that *precedes* ovulation and therefore gives the warning that is needed, and because it is precisely this change in the mucous that enables the sperm to survive and reach the egg for conception. It's this ability of the sperm to live 3 (or in very rare cases 5) days that makes it so important to know of the approach of ovulation. Knowing that you ovulated today or yesterday may just be bad news if you had intercourse the day before!

The changes in the mucous are caused by the varying levels of ovarian and pituitary hormones. They are the only dependable warning of the approach of ovulation and their recognition can become reliable after only a few cycles of observation. There are two basic changes in cervical mucous as the menstrual cycle progresses. There's a change in quantity, and also, more subtle perhaps, but even more important, a change in quality.

Let's look first at the changes in quantity.

Changes in Quantity of Mucous Through Cycle

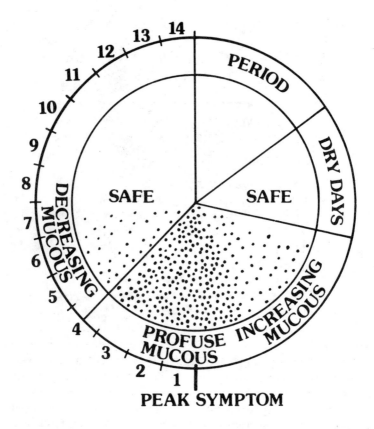

The cycle begins with a menstrual period of several days of bleeding, day 1 of the cycle being the first day of menstrual flow (spotting doesn't count). During this time even if there is some mucous present (as there can be in short cycles) it is unlikely to be detected. After bleeding finishes there are usually a few "dry" days, with no apparent discharge at the mouth of the vagina. Mucous is usually tested just inside the mouth of the vagina, as it is important to know whether there is sufficient mucous to reach this point, but in some women who have very little mucous, it may be tested at the cervix.

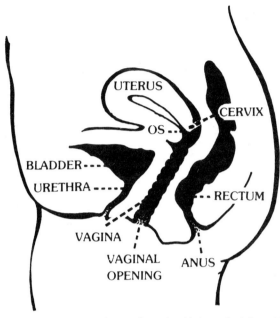

Whichever location is chosen, the readings should always be taken at the same point, or confusion will result. Some women have no "dry" days, but always have some mucous present. Just after menstruation this is likely to be scanty and sticky. In average length or long cycles there will usually be some days with either no mucous ("dry"), or this very scanty and sticky mucous, which constitute what is called the *basic infertile pattern*, evident before and after the period. In short cycles this may be missing. The cervix in fact always secretes some mucous, but during these days it may be so scanty and sticky that it does not find its way to the vaginal entrance, resulting in a "dry" experience. The walls of the vagina are always moist and give no indication of the state of the cervical mucous. Then as the cycle progresses, the mucous increases in quantity, more of it appearing at the vaginal entrance, until around ovulation it will usually be quite profuse. After ovulation it will again lessen in quantity and may disappear altogether, depending on the "Basic infertile pattern".

Occasionally there may be a showing of more profuse mucous just before bleeding starts, due to the changes in hormonal levels. This does *not* indicate a second ovulation, and is often accompanied by a drop in the temperature readings and by an experience of the pre-menstrual syndrome.

The "Now-you-see-me-now-you-don't" Ovulation

There is one other possible variation on this general pattern of increase and decrease. Occasionally a woman may have gone through all the hormonal approaches to ovulation, such as build up of mucous, and then be affected by something, such as stress or ill health, which prevents the ovulation taking place. One of two patterns may then emerge. Either she simply doesn't ovulate that month, and although the mucous may appear quite fertile, this "anovular" cycle will be evident on the temperature graph, or she may have a delayed ovulation occurring a few days later. This can result in a double peak of mucous, the first being a false peak, the second coming a few days later when the egg is actually released. It has even been known for triple peaks to occur.

Obviously if a second peak of mucous builds within a few days of apparent ovulation, precautions or abstinence must be practised in the same way as for the first.

Anovular cycles may still result in a normal period at the expected time (though the flow is sometimes reduced), whereas delayed ovulation cycles may be a little longer than usual. If these patterns are suspected, temperature readings showing the day of ovulation can confirm what is really happening.

Changes in Quality of Mucous Through Cycle

After the changes in quantity of mucous have become apparent, the changes in quality need to be distinguished.

Dry Days

Firstly we have the "dry" days with no discernable mucous at the mouth of the vagina. Mucous collected from the cervix will be very scanty, sticky and thick.

Probably Infertile Days

Then comes the thick, sticky but more profuse mucous which is called "probably infertile". This is evident externally, but very tacky, a bit like paste used for glueing paper. The chances of conception during this stage are extremely low, and about equivalent to the risks on the pill. In fact it's one of the ways in which the pill works, by causing this kind of mucous to be produced constantly. Although most women consider this a reasonable risk to take, one must be aware that some conceptions have occurred at this stage. Whether or not they were due to Lunar cycle fertility is not known. The reason this mucous is infertile is because of its consistency and texture. It forms an impenetrable plug across the cervix, a bit like a natural diaphragm, preventing the passage of the sperm into the uterus. When some is felt on the fingers, it can be seen that it is too dense, thick and sticky to allow anything through. It's simply not fluid in texture

C O N T R A C E P T I O N

at all. Also, because the sperm cannot penetrate this mucous it affords them no protection from the naturally hostile acid environment of the vagina, and they perish.

This mucous is usually yellow or white in colour, with an opaque appearance, and will form little tacky ridges when the fingers are parted, (see diagram).

Fertile Days

This mucous will then start to change, sometimes very quickly, into wet runny "fertile" mucous, becoming more fluid. This is the important change that heralds ovulation, and from this point on abstinence or protection are essential, as now the sperm may swim through and live in the mucous until ovulation occurs.

In some women this change happens over a couple of days or so and in others it may occur quite dramatically in a few hours. To guard against being unaware of a sudden change, mucous needs to be checked frequently.

When to Check Mucous

The easiest routine is to check the mucous on each visit to the toilet. This ensures frequent checking, thus avoiding sudden changes, and it's also easier to remember as a routine than trying to keep to a time-table, which can be upset by changes in daily habits (for example a regular routine built on a check at lunch time would be difficult if lunching in the park!) It's also convenient, with privacy, access to the vaginal opening and a couple of minutes to spare. Some mucous is collected on the finger tips on sitting down, and the check for quantity and quality can take the place of reading the cartoon books! After a while the routine becomes automatic and requires little thought, but initially may be confusing. If a record is made of the colour, amount and texture of the mucous, even the confused woman will be amazed at how quickly a pattern emerges on the charts. It's really only a matter of familiarisation, as with anything new. It's important not to be too concerned about the individual pattern following the classic pattern in the book — everyone's is different and unique. The important thing is for the woman to be able to recognise the changes that take place in *her* body preceding ovulation, and learn a simple vocabulary to accurately describe these.

With some women the changes are quite dramatic and obvious and with others more subtle, taking a little longer to learn. Patience is quickly rewarded, most women feeling pretty confident after about three cycles.

Mucous Checking and Intercourse

Frequent checking ensures that sudden changes are observed. It also means that when sexual excitement initiates lubrication, confusing mucous detection, a recent reading will still be reliable.

53

DRY
A little moist inside, but dry on the outside of the vagina, no dripping or staining of underwear - no sensation of wetness, lubrication or discharge.

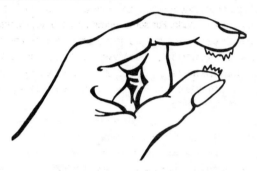

PROBABLY INFERTILE MUCOUS
Opaque yellow or white sticky, thick, pasty, tacky, (dense matter in it) holds its shape.

FERTILE MUCOUS
Thin and watery, increasing amounts, translucent (clear or milky), acellular (no dense matter), liquid, flowing, possibly pink from blood-spotting.

Residual sperm from a previous act of intercourse, with or without the addition of spermicide, can also be confusing.

This can often be a problem with morning mucous checks, most sexual activity occurring at night or first thing in the morning. Sperm will only drain out of the vagina on rising, and since different vaginas tilt at different angles, will drain at different rates. The differences between sperm, spermicide, lubrication and mucous should become evident with experience, but if in doubt 24 hours should be left before a check is made. For some women it becomes evident that they drain faster than this, but if this is a problem an emergency measure can be to wash the vagina out with warm water and wait a few hours. Constant washing or douching of the vagina is not recommended as it alters the natural environment and can give rise to yeast proliferation or Thrush. Vaginas are anyway self-cleansing, and better left alone!

This "fertile" or wet mucous is present for the whole of the fertile period. It affords protection to the sperm, so they can stay alive, channels them up into the womb, feeds them and generally aids and abets the process of conception. Sperm can easily live from the first appearance of this mucous until the egg is released. It is wet, fluid and usually clear. It may be colourless or a milky translucent white, or even pink if blood spotting occurs. Some women experience

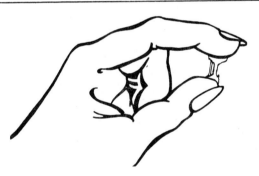

EXTREMELY FERTILE MUCOUS -'SPINN'
Profuse, stretchy quality like raw egg-white. (Called Spinn short for 'Spinnbarkeit') still wet and slippery.

it as thick, like cottage cheese, but it will still be *wet and slippery*, and it is this characteristic which is important. When some is felt on the fingers, it can be ascertained as being permeable to sperm. The quantity will increase and will continue to do so until it probably changes to the fourth stage or "spinn".

"Spinnbarkeit"

Not every woman experiences this stage of mucous, and this is not important. Indeed every woman's cycle is quite unique and may vary quite a lot from this basic pattern, different stages lasting different amounts of time, and sometimes being missed altogether.

"Spinn" is the type of mucous that resembles raw egg white. It is still wet and slippery but jelly-like in consistency, holding together and stretching so it can be "spun" from thumb to forefinger. It is not cohesive in the same way as the tacky infertile mucous, remaining wet and slippery to the touch, although holding together in a gelatinous mass. Usually clear or milky white, it can occur for anything up to a couple of days, though it often comes down as a single mass, as if an egg has been cracked open in the vagina. This often occurs whilst on the toilet which may result in it not being detected.

"Peak Symptom"

Whether "spinn" is present or not, at this stage the "Peak Symptom" is experienced. This is in a way a misnomer as it's not always the day of *most* mucous, but rather the *last* day of either type of fertile mucous (wet or spinn). It usually coincides with the day before, or the day of, ovulation, and is only recognisable retrospectively after the mucous has dried up again, or become sticky, reverting to the "basic infertile pattern". This delay in recognition is no problem, as it is necessary to leave three days after the last day of fertile mucous (peak symptom) before infertility is assured. One day is allowed in case the peak symptom occurred before ovulation, one day for the life of the egg and one day safety margin. During this three-day wait it becomes apparent that the last of the fertile mucous has been experienced. The couple is then free to make unprotected love until the next fertile period, either the next mid-cycle ovulation or the next lunar phase return. If ovulation has definitely been confirmed, the change to fertile mucous that sometimes precedes the period can safely be ignored.

Simplicity Itself

So — the mucous method is really very simple. Precautions or abstinence are employed as soon as the mucous changes, or becomes fluid and wet, until 3 days after the last day of any type of fertile mucous.

Keeping Records

Recording observations is really very important and speeds up the learning process enormously, enabling the comparison of one cycle with the next.

Don't despair if for the first few months the mucous observations seem obscure, keep checking every time you visit the toilet, and writing down the observations. It's easier to write down a *description* of colour, quantity and texture than trying to make decisions as to which type of mucous you are experiencing. This way your own unique pattern emerges, and you will soon find that the differences become clear. Just as in anything else you are unfamiliar with, subtle differences only become apparent on familiarisation. Just as your Grandmother may say "But all these pop songs sound the same to me, dear", so you will take a while to differentiate the mucous types. They will soon become familiar and it will be second nature to know where you are in your cycle. You will come to know whether you normally expect any "spinn" and when, and how many days of wet mucous to anticipate. Also whether your Basic Infertile Pattern is one of no mucous (dry days), or whether you always have some mucous present. Everyone's pattern is unique and you will become familiar with yours on seeing it repeat itself month after month, even though it differs from the "norm". Individual patterns may of course change and it cannot be expected that any situation will remain entirely consistent.

Abstinence during the first few months is helpful in learning mucous patterns more quickly, as there is less interference from residual sperm. However a rigid rule to abstain for at least one month may not be realistic. Simply be aware if any previous intercourse may have compromised the mucous readings and if in doubt, leave the reading for 24 hours, or wash out the vagina with warm water and wait a few hours (again — not too often). Condoms, which contain sperm, interfere with readings less. The more you abstain, the faster you learn (and then the less you need to abstain!). Take it at your own pace and write down *all* possible affecting conditions with your mucous record.

Although in a comprehensive approach we have several ways of diagnosing fertility, it is important not to play one method against another. If any system indicates fertility — caution is the best course.

Temperature Method

Temperature readings, although they do *not* warn of the approach to ovulation, can be extremely useful, particularly in the learning period, and as back-up at times of confusion in the mucous readings, confirming definitely that ovulation has occurred and is over. Mucous readings and their usefulness as a diagnostic technique, may be compromised in a number of situations, for example by recent sexual activity, during recovery from taking the contraceptive pill, whilst familiarisation is occurring in the first few learning months, and if sudden irregularity causes confusion. At these times it may be necessary to avoid unprotected sex during the first half of the cycle and rely on the temperature changes alone to confirm post-ovulatory infertility.

Temperature changes also help to confirm that ovulation did indeed take place, and exactly when, giving an accurate figure for the length of the luteal phase, or the second half of the cycle (which can then be used to make a more accurate rhythm calculation).

As part of the learning process temperature readings are invaluable as they help to pinpoint the exact day of ovulation, confirming where in the mucous pattern this occurred. This speeds up recognition of mucous readings, and the learning time may be much faster. Some women then discard temperature readings as a regular part of their fertility diagnosis, preferring to rely on the mucous readings. Other women prefer to keep taking the temperature readings as back up. For some women the temperature graph will show very clearly when ovulation is over, and they may feel more confident with this extra information, or it may cut down on time spent waiting to be "sure". Although one method cannot be "played off" against another, as long as the mucous is not actually fertile, and if the temperature readings indicate clearly that fertility is over, by having risen for three days, then they can be relied upon.

With temperature readings there is also a three-day wait. This time the wait is for three consecutive daily readings that are distinctly higher than the first half average reading (normally a rise of 0.3° centigrade).

As ovulation occurs, the hormonal levels produce greater heat in the body, and the body-at-rest temperature rises. This is what is measured to ascertain whether ovulation is over. In a classic temperature graph the temperature jogs along with small changes in the first half of the cycle, drops slightly just before ovulation, and then rises about half a degree centigrade and stays up until just before or during the menstrual period when it falls again. If ovulation doesn't occur then it won't go up, and if menstruation doesn't occur then it won't come down.

Because there are a number of factors that may send the temperature up, as well as these hormonal changes, it is necessary to be sure that the rise experienced is not a "freak" high caused by an infection (even slight), severe overheating in bed (e.g. leaving an electric blanket on all night), or a hangover. In order to be sure that the rise is interpreted correctly, a *sustained* rise must be visible, of three consecutive readings that are at least 0.2° centigrade higher than the average first half reading, before ovulation can be confirmed as having occurred, the egg confirmed as dead, and unprotected intercourse safe to resume. To assess the first half average reading, simply line a pencil up horizontally along the marks on the graph until it sits roughly in the middle of the spread of the readings. No mathematics required! Although the theory is that the rise should be approximately 0.3° centigrade or more, I have found that this may vary greatly from one woman to another, and becomes clearer with experience.

In diagram one the rise after ovulation is immediate and clear. It's what I call a "whoosh" chart because the temperature shoots right up in one day. The three higher readings therefore come at once on the first, second and third days after ovulation, which is the circled day at the beginning of the rise. Ovulation is always at the beginning of the rise. It's also often at the bottom of the dip, but the drop before ovulation is not always recorded as it may take place overnight and be missed on the daily reading, therefore we say ovulation is at the beginning of the rise (this means that it is not always the lowest temperature recorded in the first half).

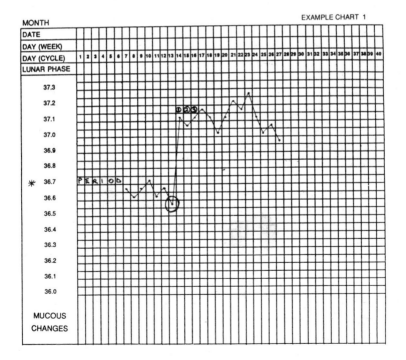

EXAMPLE CHART 1

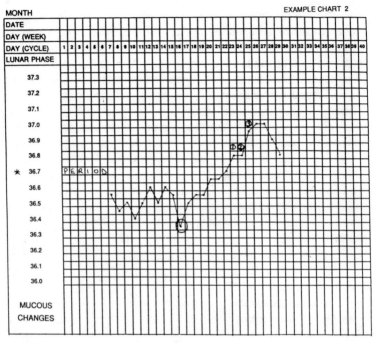

In chart number 2 there is an example of what I call a "step" chart where the rise associated with ovulation takes place over a number of days. Ovulation is still at the beginning of the rise (on the circled day), but the three distinctly higher readings will not come until several days later. This is an extreme example where it takes a week before we have higher readings 1, 2 and 3, which occur on the 7th, 8th and 9th days after ovulation, just before the temperature starts to fall again as menstruation is approached.

There are obvious differences in the usefulness of these two types of graph. For the woman who tends to have the second type of graph there's a limited functional use of temperature taking. She'll still learn on which day she ovulates, and therefore will be able to use the temperature method to refine the rhythm and mucous methods, but she will certainly have found out from her mucous readings that she is infertile again after ovulation before she reaches the third consecutive higher temperature reading. Therefore this chart is no use in giving the "all-clear" that ovulation is over, and this woman will probably discontinue taking her temperature after the first half dozen or so cycles, unless she wishes to confirm at a later date that she is ovulating or when this is occurring in her cycle. However, a woman who tends to have a chart like example No 1 will have a decision to make. Either she'll decide that

a) temperature taking is helping her learn about the "all-clear" faster than her mucous observations are and will continue to use temperature taking on a permanent basis, or

b) she will decide that although it is giving her this information, it's too much hassle and she would rather abstain for a couple of extra days a month. Alternatively she may

c) decide that although the graph gives a clear indication of the end of the fertile interval, her mucous readings are just as efficient, and therefore sufficient, or

d) decide that the graphs she is drawing up, cycle by cycle, are sufficiently consistent in shape for her to be able to interpret the middle part around ovulation time without taking temperature readings throughout the cycle. In this case she will start taking her temperature as the mucous changes indicate that ovulation is close, watch for the rise as it happens, wait for the three higher readings and then cease taking the temperature until the next cycle. This last alternative will only be a possibility with a regular cycle and temperature graph pattern, and some women prefer to take a daily reading anyway as they find a daily habit easier to maintain than a sporadic one.

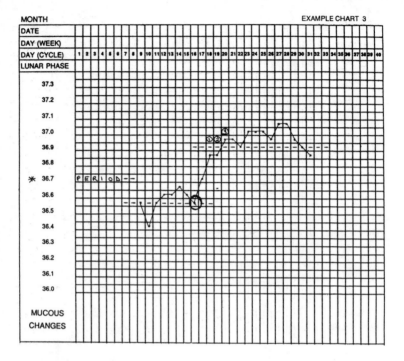

When you first look at this chart it may be difficult to distinguish the two distinct phases, as it appears to rise from the very beginning. If a chart is not visually easy to interpret, a pencil, or some straight object, may be lined up horizontally along the readings. This will nearly always clarify the chart into two distinct plateaux, or a duo-phasic pattern, with the rise between them starting at ovulation. On this chart the ovulation day is circled as in chart No 1 and I've marked in the two average temperature readings with dotted lines. The first day after ovulation the reading is not significantly higher, but days 2, 3 and 4 constitute the first, second and third higher temperatures.

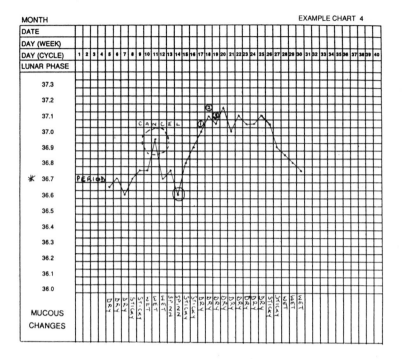

EXAMPLE CHART 4

In example 4 there is a "freak high" reading in the first half of the cycle. For some reason the temperature has risen for one day and then dropped again. The cause of this may or may not be obvious at the time of taking the temperature. This "freak" high is *not* included when the average is taken, it not being representative of a stable first half state. Also if the freak high readings were included, three significantly higher readings would be difficult to elicit. As it is, by ignoring this reading on day 11, the readings start to count on day 17. In this chart the temperature drops sharply before menstruation and this is accompanied by wet mucous as discussed earlier.

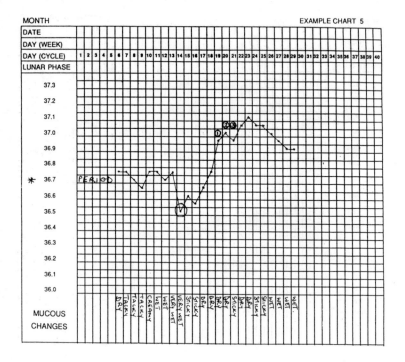

In chart number 5, the question is "Where does the rise actually start?" It would be easy to call days 14 or 16 the start of the rise. In this case the day after the dip, day 14, would be chosen. This is corroborated by the build up of wet mucous, which culminates on this day.

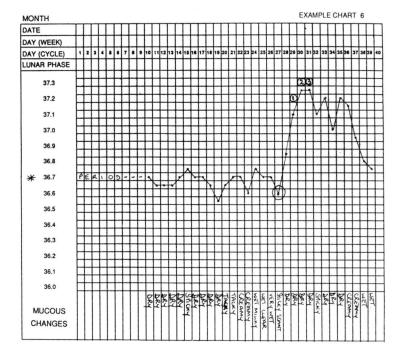

EXAMPLE CHART 6

This chart shows a long cycle with the second half remaining at approximately 14 days (here it is 13), and the first half being extended. Here there is a sharp drop again prior to the period, with wet (but not fertile) mucous present.

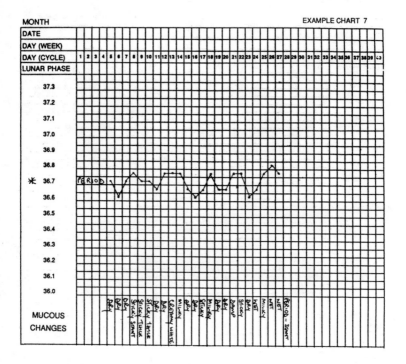

EXAMPLE CHART 7

This chart shows an "anovular" cycle, or one with no ovulation, resulting in a monophasic graph — one without a rise, and only one plateau. This can occur even though experiencing a build up of mucous, ovulation being arrested at the last minute, and may well result in a period, though this may be less profuse than usual. The only really sure test of ovulation is the temperature rise (or a blood test). An occasional cycle like this is of no concern, although frequent or persistent failure to ovulate would need attention. Fasting is a common cause of cessation of both ovulation and menstruation.

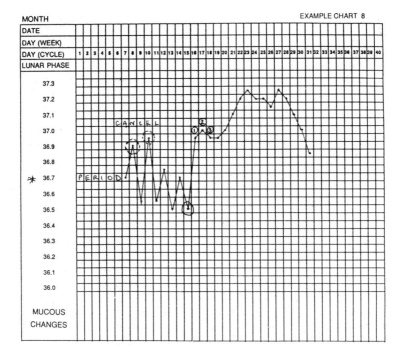

EXAMPLE CHART 8

Example 8 shows how unstable the first half can be. All freak highs are ignored when taking the average which here is indicated by the dotted line. Second halves are nearly always stable as very few things can happen which are likely to make the temperature drop.

MONTH

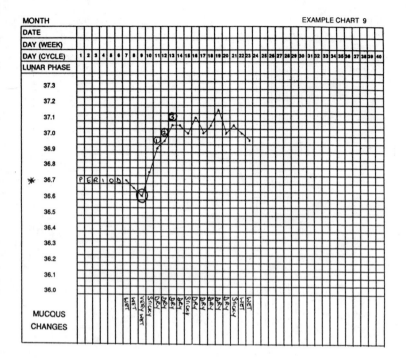

This chart shows a very short cycle, still with a 14 day second half, but with the first half ending at ovulation on day 8, and the mucous apparently being fertile as soon as bleeding ceases and possibly also on the last few days of the period. This would be a case where abstinence would have to be practised during menstruation.

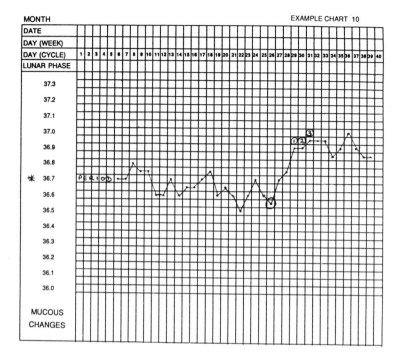

EXAMPLE CHART 10

Another long cycle in chart 10, with a 13 day second half and an extended first half which has a fairly common pattern of getting increasingly lower as ovulation is approached. This also occurs in chart 11 where it is obvious how mistakes can easily be made if care isn't exercised.

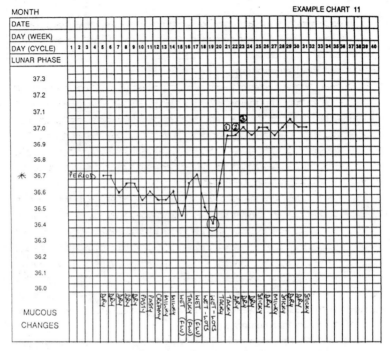

EXAMPLE CHART 11

It would have been possible for this woman to think that she had ovulated on day 15, with the next two readings being higher. There are 4 reasons why she shouldn't:

1) there are only two higher readings;

2) they're not higher than the average, only higher than the last few, because of the "descending" quality of the first half;

3) she had 'flu during the temperature rise (days 15 to 17), which would have affected the temperature and may also have delayed ovulation; and

4) she still had wet mucous.

There could be 30 higher readings but if there still was fertile mucous a risk should not be taken. The peak symptom must be *over* before temperature readings can be allowed to take precedence over the mucous observations, even if the end of the 3-day safety margin hasn't been reached. *Never* play one system off against another or pregnancy may well result.

An individual woman's chart may or may not look like one of these examples, or a mixture, but we have covered here most normal variations likely to occur.

How to Take Your Temperature
There are two different types of thermometer, a normal fever thermometer, and a "basal" or fertility thermometer. It's called a "basal" thermometer as it measures the "basal" or "body at rest" temperature. The difference in the two types is that the basal thermometer doesn't have markings higher than 39° or 40° centigrade, and therefore there is more room on the stem of the thermometer for the degrees to be marked in small gradations. This makes it easier to distinguish the small changes that are necessary.

Basal thermometers in chemists' shops are terribly expensive, and come with all sorts of unnecessary packaging and instructions that are more likely to confuse than enlighten. If these are too expensive there's one type of fever thermometer which is not quite as clear but adequate, giving an accurate enough reading. This is made by "Terumo", a Japanese company, is available in most chemist shops, and has a flat, rather than rounded, stem that happens to be fairly easy to read, and is marked in tenths of a degree rather than fifths, essential when reading to twentieths. These are generally much cheaper than the basal or fertility thermometers.

Women with no experience in reading a thermometer may need some help, but here are some clues.

The temperature is indicated by how far up the stem the mercury rises. The mercury in the bulb heats up when placed under the tongue and expands up a tiny capillary tube which can only be seen clearly through a magnifying glass. This is why the thermometer must be held at a special angle when reading it. It should be held horizontally and turned until the silver line appears. The top of the line can then be read off against the gradation which it has reached. There's a break in the mercury near the bulb, which is a constriction in the tube that prevents the mercury falling back down until the thermometer is shaken by a "flicking" motion. This means that the mercury will stay up until it is read.

To take the temperature the bulb of the thermometer is placed under the tongue in good contact with flesh, the mouth is closed and the thermometer left there for 2 to 5 minutes. Different thermometers seem to take different times to register. Experiment. Some women don't get an accurate enough reading with an oral reading and need to take it vaginally. Nearly everyone finds the reading in the mouth adequate and easier. Since the temperature is taken first thing in the morning, the thermometer is kept by the bed, and then on waking the thermometer is put in the mouth, and the 5 minutes or so waking up time spent getting the reading. Falling back to sleep can be dangerous as mouths will fall open and the reading will be false, or the thermometer will fall out and break on the floor! Then the thermometer can be put down and reading it can wait until after breakfast when eyesight may be clearer! The mercury will stay up until shaken down. After the thermometer is read it should be washed under the cold tap or wiped with a tissue. It only goes in the mouth and therefore won't need great attention. Never put it under the hot tap or it will break, and don't follow the example of one of my clients who tested it in her cup of tea and ended up with floating pieces of mercury!

The reading should be taken under the following conditions.

Firstly, before undertaking any activity. This means preferably before getting out of bed or having conversations or cups of tea, etc. If something needs to be done, for example, going to the toilet, a minimum of effort should be used and the temperature taken anyway on returning to bed. When marking it on the graph note any unusual circumstances, and then if the reading looks weird, the reason's obvious. Different women have different sensitivities and one woman might get away with leaving her bed and returning, whereas another might find that her temperature rose if she so much as said "Good morning" to somebody!

Secondly, the reading should be taken at the same time each day. The temperature is much higher later in the day, and lower earlier, regardless of how much sleep there has been. There is, fortunately, a rule for adjusting temperatures taken early and late. Adjust the reading by 0.05° centigrade (or 0.1° fahrenheit) for each hour earlier or later than the usual rising time. Since the at rest temperature will be higher if it is taken later, the reading is adjusted downward for late rising times, and upward when early. Some women have a greater or lesser variation than that given in this formula, which is based on an average woman's expectation. Experience will tell. It's necessary to avoid the freak highs associated with early rising, or the chart will end up with strange bumps in it, which are called the "Weekend syndrome"!

Thirdly, there should have been at least four hours' sleep for the body to have reached the "at rest" state, so if the night was short or disturbed, it should be noted. Generally speaking, the temperature is always taken under whatever circumstances, but these should be marked in. Other conditions to watch out for are ill-health, stress, hangovers, medication or drugs and extreme external temperature changes (such as leaving the electric blanket on all night and waking up in a sweat).

Sexual Expression at Fertile Times and Back-Up Contraception Techniques

If there is not a total commitment to the idea of abstinence at fertile times, it is useful to have access to some form of mechanical contraception which can be used when required and discarded when not. Many couples feel the need to be flexible in their approach to fertile times, and find occasional use of these techniques acceptable, whereas they may have been rejected as possible full-time methods. Certainly it is preferable to occasional risk-taking, which is what often happens when couples over-estimate their capacity to abstain. There may be occasions when the need for full sexual expression (in terms of the stability of the relationship, for example) is more important than the ideal of abstinence, and this decision is obviously the individual couple's to make. In this book I have tried to give information, rather than rules, so that these methods can be adapted to suit different needs at different times.

When the methods are fully learnt the number of fertile days in a month will vary depending on whether the lunar and hormonal cycles coincide, and on how many days of fertile, or wet, mucous the woman tends to get in a cycle. This can mean that the number of fertile days, when abstinence or contraception is required, may vary from approximately 6-12 days in a cycle. Refining mucous detection and using the Auto-suggestion techniques to help synchronisation occur can usually bring the number of days down to the lower end of this range.

However, during the first few cycles of using these methods, when mucous detection is being learnt, and there may be insufficient records of normal cycles to provide reasonable back-up from a rhythm calculation, it may be necessary to abstain, or use barrier methods of contraception more frequently than later or when confidence is greater. Obviously the methods chosen during these months will have a direct bearing on how quickly the methods (particularly mucous detection) are learnt. Any sexual activity which leaves residual fluids (semen, spermicide, lubrication) in the vagina will make the job of determining the status of the mucous harder. For this reason, it is sometimes recommended that abstinence be practised for one full cycle when these methods are first applied, in order to get a clear picture of the mucous pattern. This of course may not be possible in some circumstances and often the observations during the first cycle are not the most reliable anyway, especially if the mucous changes are slight, or if the woman has just come off the pill. Each woman (or couple) really needs to feel her way through this learning time, being aware that the more abstinence is practised the quicker learning takes place, and the less abstinence is required later. Condoms, which contain sperm and require no spermicides, are second choice, and diaphragms, with much more problem of residual fluids, least desirable. However, both during the first few cycles and later on, the choices available are as follows:

There are five ways to avoid conception during fertile times. In order of effectiveness they are abstinence, diaphragm, condom, spermicides and withdrawal.

Withdrawal
Not really effective enough. Probably better than nothing at all, but only just. Some semen is often lost before full ejaculation, and also sperm deposited on the outside of the vagina sometimes find their way in.

Spermicides
Used on their own, again not really effective enough. Although some spermicides (foams notably) claim a fairly high percentage success rate, this statistic is based on their use throughout the cycle, the majority of which is naturally infertile anyway. For use at times when the woman is highly likely to be fertile, a somewhat higher success rate is really necessary.

There is a "natural" alternative, Vitamin C, which is highly acidic, and therefore hostile to sperm. A Vitamin C tablet inserted into the vagina immobilises sperm but may only remain effective for about half an hour, ten minutes of which may be needed for it to dissolve, therefore making timing rather critical! It is necessary to obtain a tablet that is free from colouring and loosely enough packed to dissolve in the vaginal mucous and/or lubrication. It is necessary to experiment with different brands to check that this does occur, and how long it takes. If intercourse takes place over a longer period than half an hour the tablet may need to be replaced, leaving enough time for it to dissolve. Or, to avoid the problem of finding a suitable tablet, 200 mg of Vitamin C in powder form can be used. If this is mixed with slippery elm powder, which protects the mucous membranes, damage to the vagina is even less likely. The slippery elm powder (available from Health Food shops) also helps to form the basis for a paste, when mixed with water. This can be made up in bulk, and kept in an airtight jar, or formed into pessaries.

Some research was conducted in Ukrania, with three hundred women over a two year period, who inserted a 200mg Vitamin C tablet into the vagina 10 minutes before intercourse. Contraception was 96% effective. This, however, is the only research conducted so far, and although it seems highly probable that Vitamin C is preferable to chemical spermicides, no research has yet been done into the effects of Vitamin C on the vagina. It would be more effective to use Vitamin C in conjunction with a diaphragm (see below). Spermicides can be obtained at chemists' shops. Be careful to check if there is an allergic reaction before use. Spermicides have been shown to have undesirable side effects when used frequently. Everyone must use their own judgement.

Condoms
The "theoretical" success rate of condoms is very high (99%). This means that they will be effective *if used correctly*. Most problems come from care not being taken in their use, which is perhaps less of a problem if they only need to be used occasionally (infertility being confidently diagnosed for much of the cycle and probably some degree of abstinence undertaken at fertile times). Also it is highly probable that a woman or couple sufficiently motivated to use natural methods of fertility diagnosis will also be motivated to use a barrier method correctly. The actual failure rate, because of human error, is quite high (13-30%).

Its advantages are that it is easily available (at chemists' shops) and can be used without spermicides, which some people are allergic to. It also facilitates mucous detection, as sperm is contained. This is only so however if it is used without spermicides, as these will also cause confusion. It is advisable to withdraw fairly soon after ejaculation, to avoid seepage of semen from the base of the condom, and to hold the condom firmly down to the base of the penis during withdrawal, which should take place before the penis loses its erection. Space should be left at the head of the condom for the sperm when ejaculated, and the condom fitted *at the beginning of intercourse*, as some semen is usually lost before ejaculation. Condoms have other advantages of protecting against disease, more and more a real concern these days, and allowing the male partner to play a part in, and take some responsibility for, contraception.

Its disadvantages are that it must be fitted after the penis is distended, thus interfering in the spontaneity of foreplay, and that it completely covers the penis, thus inhibiting tactile experience.

Condoms deteriorate with age, so check the "use by" date, two years old is the limit. Also check that the brand bought is approved by the A.S.A. (Australian Standards Association) or equivalent body in other countries. This means that less than 0.1% of them have burst during very vigorous testing.

Diaphragms
The success rate of diaphragms is similar to that of condoms, although they are quoted as having a theoretical success rate of 98%, which is slightly lower. However the actual failure rate (due to error) is not so high (15-25%). The advantages of a diaphragm are that it allows greater spontaneity, as it can be fitted an hour or so before intercourse, in privacy, and that once inserted it is scarcely felt by either partner (if it has been fitted correctly), and does not interfere with the tactile experience. It also gives the woman more control over

contraception, in a situation where the relationship is uncertain or the partner unco-operative. It is reusable time after time, but should be checked regularly for deterioration in the rubber, and refitted every two years, and after considerable weight change or pregnancy. A diaphragm needs to be the correct size (it should be fitted by a doctor or at a clinic) and it is essential that it is inserted correctly (over the cervix) as it can easily slip in the wrong way, giving no protection.

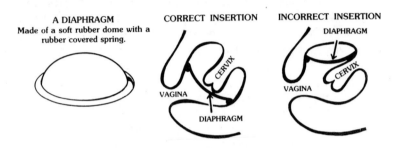

A DIAPHRAGM
Made of a soft rubber dome with a rubber covered spring.

CORRECT INSERTION
CERVIX
VAGINA
DIAPHRAGM

INCORRECT INSERTION
DIAPHRAGM
CERVIX
VAGINA

It is essential to make absolutely sure that when the right size is fitted it is demonstrated how to insert the diaphragm properly, and *how to check that this is correctly done*, by feeling the bump of the cervix through the soft rubber dome of the diaphragm with a finger. If it is inserted incorrectly it will not prevent the passage of sperm through the cervix into the womb, and it might as well be worn as a hat! Unbelievably, many Doctors do not give this information, and unless the Doctor/patient relationship is well established, and one of good communication, a women's clinic may be preferable.

One of the disadvantages of a diaphragm is that, to be sure of maximum effectiveness, the choice may be to use it in conjunction with a spermicide. This is usually a cream, jelly or foam smeared on to the diaphragm before insertion, which helps prevent the passage of the sperm around the edge of the diaphragm, and kills the sperm left in the vagina before the diaphragm is removed. However Vitamin C can also be used (see above), if preferred, the paste being used in the same way as the chemical spermicide, or a tablet being inserted above and below the diaphragm. Diaphragms are often used without spermicides, and most family planning clinics now claim that this is a safe procedure. It is recommended that if no spermicide is used the diaphragm is left in place for at least 12 hours (maximum of 24) after intercourse, instead of the 6-8 hours recommended when a chemical spermicide is used, to allow time for the sperm which is unprotected by the cervical mucous to die in the acidic vagina. This means that cervical mucous cannot be observed during this time. This is another disadvantage of a diaphragm, which also interferes greatly with mucous observations owing to the residual sperm and maybe spermicide left in the vagina. An emergency measure is to douche (with warm water) and then wait for the mucous to collect before observation. This cannot be done too frequently as the pH balance of the vagina will be altered, and the yeast-gobbling bacteria removed, encouraging yeast infections. *Frequent* use of the diaphragm is therefore incompatible with mucous observance. If a diaphragm is the only acceptable form of contraception at fertile times, and is used frequently, rhythm calculation can be used to warn of the approach of ovulation, and temperature readings would need to be used for determining the end of the fertile period.

Abstinence

Totally effective! And not necessarily difficult. Most couples find abstinence for a few days each month not nearly such a problem as they anticipate. There is much physical sexual expression which does not rely on full intercourse, and this time can be an opportunity to be quite creative (rather than pro-creative!). Also the full sexual act can be appreciated more fully when resumed after a few days.

Many couples feel that in order to really "tune in" to their natural cycles, they need to abstain from full sexual intercourse at fertile times as they feel that it is inappropriate except if conception is desired.

Reminders

Always be aware that semen and spermicides and even, to a lesser extent, lubrication, look very like fertile mucous, and while either of them are present no competent assessment can be made of the state of the mucous. It is therefore inadvisable to use these techniques too often while mucous checking is being relied upon to diagnose fertility.

One of the reasons why many of these barrier methods fail is that they are neglected because the user becomes intolerant of them. If they are only being used occasionally during fertile times (or in extreme situations for the first half of the cycle until the basal body temperature has risen for three days), this becomes less of a deterrent to their effective use. However always remember that there is a greater risk when using anything other than abstinence and all statistics given for effectiveness of natural methods are taken from cases where abstinence was practised at *all* fertile times.

Whatever protection is chosen at fertile times, making mutual and responsible decisions that are appropriate for the circumstances will enhance most relationships, bringing couples closer together and helping to make them more sexually and physically aware.

Summary of Effective Rates of Birth Control Methods

Method	Lowest Possible Rate of Pregnancy	Actual Rate of Pregnancy
Condom	1%	13-30%
Diaphragm*	2%	15-25%
Spermicide	5%	25-29%
Withdrawal	10%	23%

* statistics taken from use with spermicide.

Coming Off the Pill and After Childbirth
These two situations present some problems for the novice who is just starting to use natural fertility methods.

Because of the.false state of pregnancy the body is in whilst on the pill, the body can take a while to settle back into normal habits. Some effects can be

a) a lack of periods,

b) a lack of ovulation or

c) a lack of discernible mucous changes. Natural therapies such as acupuncture, homoeopathy, herbal medicine and vitamin and mineral therapy can be effectively used to get the reproductive system working again as quickly as possible. In a few cases, especially if left untreated, amennorrhoea (lack of periods) or other hormonal disturbances resulting in anovular cycles or insufficient mucous can result in temporary and even permanent sterility. Therefore, with all my clients who are coming off the pill I immediately put them onto a course of herbal remedies and vitamin/mineral supplementation. At the beginning of this chapter we looked at the vitamins and minerals that are deficient in pill takers. Most of these are usefully combined in the combination pills marketed for P.M.T. My basic herbal formula (alterations and additions being made for individual situations) is as follows:

F.E. Chaste Tree (Vitex Agnus Castus)

F.E. False Unicorn Root (Helonias)

F.E. True Unicorn Root (Aletris)

F.E. St. Marys Thistle (Silybum Marianum)

F.E. Golden Seal (Hydrastis Canadensis)

(F.E. stands for Fluid Extract — the most convenient way to combine herbs in individual formulas.)

This stimulates normal functioning of the pituitary and ovarian glands, normal mucous secretions, and removal of residual chemicals from the liver. With this approach a speedy resumption of normal reproductive functions is greatly assisted.

However, between using the pill and employing natural methods effectively there is an unavoidable time when neither method is applicable. Most women when they embark on natural methods back up their mucous observations with the use of the calculations of the rhythm method, until they feel secure that they are competent in distinguishing the different types. Unfortunately when first coming off the pill the rhythm method calculations cannot be made as there is no history of a natural cycle to base them on. The mucous changes may also take a while to settle down to a recognisable pattern. Therefore there will be a period of several cycles until either there is confidence in the ability to tell from body symptoms when fertility is present or there have been enough consecutive and regular cycles to make a fairly accurate calculation with the rhythm method.

During this time there is really no alternative to either abstinence or a barrier technique, at least until the basal temperature has risen each month for three consecutive days, indicating that ovulation has occurred. The disadvantage of using any method involving spermicides is that they mask mucous changes (as does semen), thus delaying the learning process.

The choice is therefore to abstain (or possibly use a condom without spermicide, as this will contain the semen), for at least the first half of several cycles until confidence is established in distinguishing the mucous changes, or to decide to use a condom or a diaphragm (with or without a spermicide) for the first few months until the cycle has re-established sufficiently to make rhythm calculations. Then abstinence can be restricted to calculated fertile days over the next few cycles as the mucous changes are learned. Again the Basal Temperature Chart can still be effective in giving the "all clear" after ovulation.

The more effort that is made to learn the mucous changes, and the faster this is achieved, the sooner the number of days when fertility is suspected can be reduced to those where it is definitely known to be present.

After childbirth, many women remain infertile during breastfeeding, but even so this will not delay the return of the menstrual cycle indefinitely. Some women find that they menstruate quite soon even though they are feeding their babies. The return of periods and ovulation will be slower if sucking is frequent. As soon as night feeds are missed, for example, or bottles used to supplement, then the return of the menstrual cycle is more likely. Sexual activity also seems to precipitate return of the menses. However each woman is different in this regard, though the pattern is often the same in each pregnancy.

Unfortunately the first ovulation precedes the first period, so it is essential to keep a watch for mucous changes which will warn of the onset of fertility.

Sometimes ovulation attempts to re-establish itself several times before it manages to do so. There may be mucous changes in these instances that do not result in ovulation or in a subsequent period. Also, if natural birth control methods have not been practised before, there may be several false alarms. It is important that *any* change in the vaginal mucous which could be interpreted as a change to fertile mucous is followed by three days abstinence, or contraception. The first few cycles may be a bit irregular, so beware of making rhythm calculations based on insufficient data. Remember that basal body temperature readings will corroborate the mucous findings.

Unprotected intercourse on Lunar Phase fertile days should be avoided from six weeks after childbirth as the ability to ovulate spontaneously may precede the return of the hormonal cycle.

Charting

Apart from the records of mucous changes and temperature graphs, many women find it helpful to keep an account of other changes that they experience as they go through their cycle.

On the next page is a chart that gives room to record both the essential diagnostic symptoms, and also some of the more subtle changes that may help the woman to tune in to her cycle, and recognise some of its effects. For example, if patterns emerge in the "energy" and "emotional state" observations, then it may become clear why certain states are experienced. Then if treatment is required it can be more effective, and natural "highs" and "lows" accommodated. It is often interesting to see if the "sexual desire" column matches up with fertile times (both hormonal and lunar) and also to notice if intercourse follows the woman's desire pattern or her partner's. "CERVIX CHANGES" refers to the position and condition of the cervix, which becomes soft, high, open and wet (S.H.O.W.) around ovulation, and hard, low, shut and dry (H.L.S.D.) at infertile times. Not all of these observations are necessary, but each woman comes to her own optimum level of recording, which gives her both an effective contraceptive programme and useful information about her mind/body states of health.

As the cycle's symptoms are understood more thoroughly then confidence increases, and even irregular cycles need not be of concern. Most women find that the feeling of control and involvement that these methods bring give great relief from anxiety. Knowing that confident contraception can be practised without abusing the health of the body can only benefit the woman, her partner and their relationship.

For those couples who are aware enough of their physical and emotional needs to choose these methods, responsible use of them should be easy. It is important to remain aware of the desire to have children, so that a continual conscious decision is made to wait for the right time, and not to subconsciously "forget" that fertility is present!

Children are precious — may all yours come when they are welcome.

MONTH																																									
DATE																																									
DAY (WEEK)																																									
DAY (CYCLE)	1	2	3	4	5	6	7	8	9	10	11	12	13	14	15	16	17	18	19	20	21	22	23	24	25	26	27	28	29	30	31	32	33	34	35	36	37	38	39	40
LUNAR PHASE																																									
37.3																																									
37.2																																									
37.1																																									
37.0																																									
36.9																																									
36.8																																									
36.7																																									
36.6																																									
36.5																																									
36.4																																									
36.3																																									
36.2																																									
36.1																																									
36.0																																									
CONDITIONS AFFECTING TEMPERATURE																																									
MUCOUS CHANGES amount, colour, texture																																									
OVULATION PAINS. LEFT OR RIGHT																																									
CERVIX CHANGES (S.H.O.W.) (H.L.S.D.)																																									
SORE BREASTS																																									
GREASY SKIN AND HAIR																																									
ENERGY PEAKS																																									
EMOTIONAL STATE																																									
SEXUAL DESIRE																																									
INTERCOURSE																																									
BLEEDING																																									

6 CONCEPTION

For most of us during our active sexual lives the issue we primarily concern ourselves with is contraception. Even for those of us who do decide to have children, the occasions when conception is actually sought are few and far between unless there is a problem with fertility. The result of this is that in nearly all our sexual experiences we are "holding back" from one of the more obvious consequences of the sexual act. All the more reason, therefore, to plan and consciously enjoy the few times in our lives when we give an unqualified "Yes" to the sexual experience in its entirety. A child consciously conceived and welcomed in this way cannot but benefit from the parents' emotional state surrounding its beginnings.

So often pregnancies, even when welcomed, are only confirmed after several weeks have lapsed, during which time the baby has been developing extremely fast, without the conscious participation of either parent. Many more are "mistakes" to which the parents later become reconciled, to some degree or other. In this case there is often a panic reaction to the realisation of the conception, many women having a deeply ingrained fear of pregnancy, which sometimes cannot be overcome even when a child is planned. The child's psychic and psychological connections with the mother, and also, to a lesser degree perhaps in these early stages, with the father, are of paramount importance in the development of the baby, and to conceive consciously and optimistically and to be "with" the child from the very beginning can provide the very best environment for healthy growth. This fear of pregnancy is of course a contaminating factor in a great many sexual encounters, and can only be overcome in the presence of a trusted birth control program which allows confident prediction of conception. Natural birth control methods offer this in that they "de-mystify" the reproductive processes and hand the control of them back to the individual.

It is every woman's right to have control over her own fertility to the greatest degree possible, without endangering her own mental or physical health, and this can only be achieved by her understanding how her reproductive system works. Nature provides us with marvellous and unmistakable signs of fertility which we can learn to recognise, interpret, and then use to avoid or achieve pregnancy.

In this way, if a child is desired, the parents can prepare mentally, emotionally and physically for the conception and ensure that the optimum conditions surround this most important of events. By understanding the physical processes involved in the timing of conception optimum use can also be made of low fertility in either partner, which can often result in success without recourse to treatment.

There are many natural therapies which can be effective for infertility and low fertility states, which have none of the possible side-effects, such as multiple births, that may result from the use of fertility drugs. Drugs interfere with the hormonal balances of the body in a drastic manner, and apart from the physical implications, this can often result in far reaching emotional changes.

The most important natural aid to fertility, whether there is a problem or merely a desire for awareness, is the timing of conception. In cases of viable fertility levels, the woman's state is usually more critical than the man's, she being either fertile (for a few days each month) or not, whereas he will be relatively fertile all the time, though (as we saw in Chapter 4) this may peak at his lunar return. In cases of low fertility, however, the problem may lie with either, or both, partners. Although some surveys put the female's share of infertility problems as high as 70%, there are other surveys which give the male partner a greater responsibility. However, in any cases where there is a conception problem, the man's fertility will usually be tested first, as it is both easier to do, with much less intrusive and painful (though sometimes embarrassing!) procedure involving no surgery or possible side-effects and is also much more conclusive. The tests for women's fertility, or joint compatibility, can be much more complex, traumatic, and less definitive.

With a man's fertility, the semen is tested for sperm count (number of sperm), mobility (ability to propel themselves) and motility (number of sperm still active after a few hours). All of these factors need to be at certain levels, which has been explained more fully in Chapter 4.

If the woman's fertility is suspect, then she can also elect to have various tests. These range from the simple blood tests to check hormone levels, to surgical procedures. Many women who come to me have already been through a whole barrage of tests and have either identified the problem, or may still be left with no reasons for their apparent infertility. Other women come to me before they embark on these procedures, and usually will wait to get some initial "answers" from their temperature and mucous charting before going any further.

Whether there are problems or not, whether they have been identified or not and whether they originate with the male or female partner, the first step is always to look at the timing of conception.

For those who have normal fertility levels this is critical so they can be sure which sexual event is the one which starts it all, and so they can avoid conception until entirely ready. They may indeed desire to spend some time preparing for conception, especially if health levels are not optimum, or the woman has just come off the pill. In these cases 3-6 months of natural contraception methods (possibly combined with barrier methods) can be used in conjunction with naturopathic measures designed to "detoxify" the body, eliminate all traces of the chemical hormones from the liver, and restore healthy levels of all nutrients. Then, having become adept at identifying the time of maximum fertility, conception can be approached with a high degree of certainty.

For those who have unidentified fertility problems, it is always possible that correct timing may be all that is required. In cases of low fertility, with only a very few days each month where conception can take place, and the chances on each of those days lower than normal, it only needs a busy lifestyle, one or other partner to be tired or have a "headache", and months or even years can go by without success. The average time taken for conception, contrary to most peoples' belief, is several (4-6) months.

Conversely, if the sperm count is on the low side, though still viable, too frequent lovemaking can be the problem, with not enough time allowed to regenerate a sufficiently high sperm count between sexual acts.

Timing for conception is of course a bit like timing for contraception in reverse, and knowing the fertile times is a big step forward in planning the time of conception (see Chapter 5 for details). There are, however, many ways of making sure that this information is used with optimum effectiveness.

The Life Span of the Egg and the Sperm

Sperm have been known to live up to 5 days given the right conditions. It is usually considered, however, that they are by then somewhat geriatric and unable (or at least unlikely) to hobble their way to the egg. Most studies give 3 days as the maximum viable life-span of the sperm. This, of course, also relies on environmental conditions. As we discussed in the previous chapter, adequate amounts of the right type of mucous are necessary both to protect the sperm from the acidity in the vagina, and to nourish and guide them up into the cervix and the womb. Since this mucous is usually present before the mid-cycle ovulation, and perhaps triggered by a spontaneous ovulation (see Chapter 3), the sperm can be ready and waiting for the egg as it comes down the fallopian tube, even if deposited a couple of days before ovulation takes place.

The egg, however, only lasts normally from 12-24 hours. So, if ovulation happened in the morning, and intercourse that evening, the egg might already be dead! Therefore it is vital to know *in advance* that ovulation is about to take place. Information that ovulation has *already* taken place (such as that given by basal temperature readings) will be useless if there is any chance that it happened up to, or more than, 12 hours ago, or if there is no opportunity for intercourse in the next 12 hours.

Conception on the Hormonal Cycle

Obviously the best way to tell that the woman is about to ovulate, and ready to receive sperm, is through the mucous observations (see Chapter 5). Once fertile mucous has been detected, there is a good chance that sperm deposited in the vagina will be ready and waiting for the egg when it is released. However this procedure can be improved upon.

By using a combination of temperature taking (again see Chapter 5) and mucous observations over several cycles, it is possible to come to a refined understanding of the woman's ovulation timing within her mucous pattern. Often there is a regular mucous pattern preceding the release of the egg, as defined (fairly accurately, to within a day) by the beginning of the temperature rise. A woman may find that she generally ovulates on "The third day of wet mucous" or "usually the fifth" or "the second day of spinn, following three to four days of wetness". Personal repeating patterns are often uncovered in this way, and "Mittelschmirtz" (German for "pain in the middle") — a dull ache or sharp pain often associated with ovulation — can help to confirm this. We cannot necessarily expect to pinpoint ovulation to the exact day, but we can, retrospectively over several cycles, refine our understanding considerably.

This can make a great deal of difference in some cases. For example a woman who generally had 5 days of wet mucous, followed by one day of spinn, followed by a return to dry sticky mucous, might determine that she probably ovulated on the day after the spinn-type mucous. Since the day *before* ovulation is the most important day for intercourse, she might avoid sexual activity for at least 4 of the "wet" days, in order to conserve sperm, and concentrate on the fifth day of wetness and the day of "spinn". Or, if the pattern was entirely regular, go even further and only use the "spinn" day. Without this information she might have started her attempts 5 days before, when the wetness started, and wasted valuable sperm. This is especially important if the sperm count is at all low.

Even if the pattern changes suddenly and ovulation is missed that cycle, it is better to concentrate on the optimum day and pinpoint it accurately on even a few cycles, than continually lessen the chance of sufficient sperm being present on the right day by using the extended time over and over again.

Temperature readings obviously do not, in themselves, give us this warning of ovulation. However they are an essential part of the process of refining the understanding of the significance of the individual's mucous pattern. Also, of course, they confirm that ovulation is indeed taking place, how long the "luteal phase" or second half of the cycle is, and on which day of the cycle the egg is usually released.

In this way we gather more essential information. If ovulation does not occur, or only happens rarely, then therapy is indicated. Natural approaches can be very effective, but beware of "self-help"! Although the individual woman or couple has a vital role to play in fertility awareness, and should be encouraged to play as active, informed and responsible role as possible, fertility is very complex and treatment is much more likely to be effective if supervised by a reputable therapist. Herbal medicine, vitamin and mineral therapy, dietary measures, homoeopathy, acupuncture and even psychotherapy all have a part to play. We will look at this in more detail later in this chapter.

If the temperature readings indicated a very short Luteal Phase — or second half of the cycle, from ovulation to menstruation — again, therapy is required. In this case there is probably a lack of progesterone, and not enough time for the egg to implant in the womb.

Information about the usual length of the second half of the cycle is useful if we want to use a rhythm calculation to help timing. The main difficulty here is that, because the accuracy is so easily undermined by changes in the cycle, it is difficult to narrow the fertile days down to a very few each month. This means that the sperm get spread out over a longer period of time, thus reducing their effectiveness. Accurate awareness of conception then becomes guesswork because any number of attempts over several days could have been successful. If the temperature readings show a fairly consistent day for the beginning of the rise, this information may be used instead of a conventional rhythm calculation.

Conception on the Lunar Cycle
As more fully outlined in Chapter 10, there are 4 days of possible and potential fertility each lunar month on this cycle, though much of this time is to account for sperm life. If intercourse happened at the beginning of the 4-day interval the sperm could live through to the peak time when ovulation might occur. However, unless this cycle coincides with the hormonal fertile time, the ovulation will need to be triggered, and happen spontaneously. This event seems most likely to occur as the result of sexual activity *within the 24 hours preceding the exact return of the natal angle*. If intercourse took place 2 days before this, then the ovulation would be unlikely to occur. So, when conception is desired, it is preferable to make love within this 24 hours. Intercourse is then likely to trigger the release of the egg, and deposit the sperm simultaneously. To this end, sexual activity can be frequent, the greater the stimulation the more likely the ovulation, and the timespan being within the viable life of the sperm.

So a typical 4-day lunar fertile time looks like this:

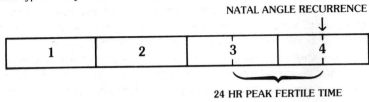

The natal angle recurrence is the time when the sun/moon angle is exactly the same as at the woman's birth.

Again, as in the hormonal cycle, a few days' abstinence prior to the conception attempt will build up the sperm count. We will talk more about preparation for conception later.

Some women conceive more easily at their mid-cycle ovulation and some on their lunar cycle, which remains fertile wherever it falls in relation to the menstrual cycle, but it seems that in nearly all cases fertility is enhanced when they synchronise.

Synchronisation of Cycles
We talked in Chapter 3 of how some women conceive when menstruation and lunar fertility coincide. This does seem to be a fairly "potent" combination for some, and in that chapter I gave some examples. It seems an unlikely time for conception to occur, and I know of no research on the reasons for it.

A possible explanation would be that a spontaneous ovulation triggers hormonal changes and that these prepare the endometrium in the 3-5 days the fertilised egg spends in the tube before coming down into the womb. This theory is supported by some feedback that I have had from experienced clients of mine, who, adept at recognising signs of ovulation, experience these, including changed mucous and "Mittelschmirtz", when either trying to conceive or using protection at the lunar fertile time. Although at this stage this theory is only conjecture, the evidence that the conceptions do indeed occur is quite widespread.

Fertility seems to peak even more dramatically for many women if they experience their regular hormonal cycle ovulation at their lunar phase return (i.e. when their 2 fertile times coincide). This synchronisation of cycles is what we aim for when the woman's fertility is suspect or low.

The most effective way to achieve this synchronisation is through suggestion. Auto suggestion techniques, or hypotherapy can be used, as we discussed in Chapter 3. Women can either create the positive visualisations and affirmations for themselves, listen to a tape on which a prepared text is spoken by either themselves or a therapist, or receive treatment from a hypnotherapist on a regular basis. These suggestions are often extremely effective, and are most likely to succeed if used with conviction and regularity.

In cases where the sperm count is low a decision may be made to synchronise the woman's hormonal cycle with the male partner's lunar fertility peak. This is achieved in exactly the same way, merely replacing the man's lunar return time (2 days after new moon, for example) for the woman's (see Chapter 4).

In extremely lucky instances the 2 partners' lunar cycles may coincide or be very close, and then this choice need not be made.

The only time when synchronisation is not desirable is when sex selection or viability is of concern. We will discuss these further in Chapter 8, but the reasons for avoiding the coincidence of the two cycles are simple. Both sex selection (when related to the sign of the moon present at conception) and viability (when similarly related to the astrological configurations) are better controlled by knowing the *exact* time of conception. On the lunar cycle this is taken as the exact time of the natal angle return, whereas on the menstrual cycle one cannot be so definite. It is therefore easier to ascertain the astrological configurations and moon sign present at conception if it occurs on the lunar cycle, as distinct from the mid-menstrual ovulation. The lunar cycle remains fertile wherever it falls in the ovulation cycle, but fertility seems to be enhanced by their synchronicity.

Preparation for Conception

Preparation for conception can be the factor that both makes it a possibility, and ensures a successful ensuing pregnancy. There is both the long and short term to be considered. Long term preparation is necessary to ensure that health is good in both partners before conception is attempted. Not only will this increase the chances of success in conception but will also be of paramount importance to the health of mother and child throughout pregnancy and the successful growth and development of the foetus. The demands on the mother's body are enormous during pregnancy, nutrients normally going first to the developing baby. It is difficult to build up reserves of nutrients once the pregnancy is underway, and therefore important to do so before conception occurs.

Fertility is also affected greatly by the state of health in both partners, and diet, exercise and medication or supplements should be monitored by a competent therapist.

Diet preference is a very personal affair, and may be affected by ethical or religious convictions as well as health considerations. What suits one individual may not suit another, and different situations call for different measures, so we can only give very general guidelines here.

One golden rule is to eat as fresh, freshly prepared and wide a variety of food as possible. Vegetarians need to be extremely careful about their protein levels. Protein is extremely important for fertility. If meat is not eaten then fish is an excellent source of protein without, in most cases, problems of high levels of saturated fats and cholesterol. Some people who prefer not to eat red meats, are happy to eat white meats, such as chicken. Battery-raised chickens are not advisable as they have extremely high levels of chemicals, including steroids, antibiotics and other drugs. Fortunately free-range chickens are becoming more widely available. If no meat or fish is eaten then adequate protein is more difficult to include in the diet without using excessive amounts of dairy products (too high in saturated fats and a source of allergic reaction for many). Nuts and soy products are the other best solutions, but if in doubt consult a naturopath or nutritionist. Smoking should be entirely avoided (this has been shown to be harmful to a healthy sperm count) and sugar, salt, tea and coffee kept to a minimum. Watercress is high in many of the useful nutrients, and is a useful addition to salads. It's probably advisable to use some supplements. It would be nice to say that all essential nutrients could be acquired from the diet, but in these days of dubious cultivation techniques and long shelf-life this cannot unfortunately be relied upon.

The vitamins and minerals most important for female fertility and reproductive health are:- Vitamins A, B group (especially B1 & B6), C and E. Calcium and zinc are very important for healthy mucous production. Calcium helps the stretchiness of the mucous, and the sperm to swim. It is also important for uterine muscle tone, and counteracts the negative effect of manganese in the vagina which can cause the mucous to become sticky. Zinc improves reproductive tone generally, and mucous production. It is generally present in semen. A low iron level can adversely affect the mucous membranes, magnesium is helpful for muscle tone, and potassium chloride for hormonal health.

There are several combination tablets, marketed for the relief of the pre-menstrual syndrome which have most or all of these constituents. The Chinese herbs Dong-quai and Fo-ti-tieng are available from health food stores, as are various combinations of Anglo-American traditional herbs. However it is greatly preferable to consult with a therapist who can tailor any medication to the individual's needs and condition. We will look in a while at how natural medicine can overcome some common infertility problems.

For male fertility it is extremely important to avoid hot baths, tight pants, or exposing the testes to heat or pressure, as these kill sperm. This is the reason that the testes hang outside the body, as even body temperature is too high. I have known cases of male infertility to be attributable to sitting on a warm engine for long hours each day, and frequently wearing a wetsuit!

Important vitamins and minerals for the male are Vitamins C (important for motility), B12 and E, and zinc. Ginseng, Bee pollen and Octocosonal (an extract from wheat germ oil, which is also high in Vitamin E) are also useful. No smoking in cases of low sperm count.

See Chapter 4 for my basic herbal formula for problems with sperm count.

Exercise is also important, for both partners. One very good way of exercising for those with a busy lifestyle is to use a rebounder. These mini-trampolines relax and tone the internal organs and achieve lymphatic drainage and detoxification as well as increasing fitness. One word of warning: there are many varieties on the market, at a great variation in price. The important thing is to have a rebounder that gives a good firm bounce and doesn't deteriorate and sag with age. One way to ensure this is to buy the most expensive and high quality version. Another is to check the spring construction.

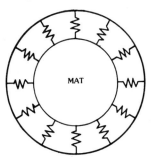

Trampoline spring
Construction to avoid

Springs arranged like this tend to stretch with time, as the strain is always taken across the mid-point.

Trampoline spring
Construction to choose

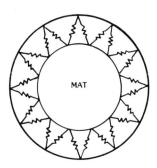

Springs arranged like this take the strain across different parts of the mat and generally remain taut.

Of course the cheaper versions, even if they have the right spring construction, may be less hard-wearing.

Swimming and walking are also excellent forms of exercise, though these require a little more time to achieve regularly.

Having acquired a reasonable state of health, then short-term preparation for conception needs also to be considered.

I have already mentioned that sperm count can be enhanced by 3-5 days of abstinence before the conception attempt. Longer periods of abstinence can in fact be counter-productive.

Many attempts to conceive in apparently fertile situations are unsuccessful because of tension and negative attitudes. Psychological blocks are as real and effective as physical ones, and we will look at some of the available therapies later on in this chapter. However there are a number of useful and harmless self-help techniques that can be applied to help relaxation and the joyful and positive approach to conception.

During the 3-5 days of abstinence preceding each conception attempt, the couple can join each other in positive meditations and visualisations of a successful outcome. In cases of infertility it's very easy to become disheartened by repeated failure, and to either lose all hope, or to cut off emotionally altogether. Some time is well spent quietly sitting together visualising in as much detail as possible a successful conception, pregnancy and birth. This can be added to the auto-suggestions used to synchronise the cycles, as described in Chapter 3, and either created out loud, internally, or listened to on a tape prepared by either partner or a therapist.

In Chapter 3 I gave some suggestions for a visualisation of the cycles synchronising and the egg being released. It's an easy continuation to see the sperm being implanted in the vagina, swimming through the fertile mucous up to the cervix, through the uterus, into the tube and dancing around the egg. One sperm is then seen to fertilise the egg which eventually comes down into the womb and implants in the uterine wall. Growth then occurs, with the foetus becoming recognisably human (quite perfect, and of a particular sex if required). The baby grows, the womb expands, the belly swells. Everything continues to full term when the beautiful baby is ready to be born. Then the cervix dilates, the uterus contracts and the child is pushed in rhythmic surges through the birth canal. Hands of willing and loving "helpers" aid the child out into the world with smiles all round, and the baby is handed to the mother (by the father if appropriate) and put to the breast.

A useful verbal affirmation might then be:-

"I will ovulate on my hormonal cycle 3 days after the full moon (if, for example, this is when the woman's lunar return falls) and I will continue to do so cycle after cycle until I conceive. I will conceive a healthy child and give birth to it (him/her) easily, after a successful pregnancy."

This can be adapted in cases of low male fertility to affirm the production of plentiful sperm and their life in the female reproductive tract. Also, possibly, the synchronisation of the female ovulation with the male lunar cycle.

Relaxation and positivity can also be assisted by touch and massage. Especially during times of abstinence it is important not to lose this support of physical contact in the relationship. Lots of cuddles and massage of tension spots such as neck, shoulders, face, head and feet can be very helpful. However inexpert one may feel, there is always enormous benefit, even from touching. Massage can also be used to lead into a relaxed sexual situation at the conception attempt. Especially useful here is massage of the tummy, where much emotional tension collects. The peristaltic motion of the intestine is the only body function which speeds up as we relax, and a gurgling tummy can be a good indication of stress release. To encourage negative energy to discharge through this process, this simple version of a "Peristaltic" massage is easily adapted to home use.

(1) The person being massaged lies on their back, breathes deeply but gently and relaxes from their toes to their head.

(2) The "masseur" strokes down from the diaphragm to the base of the tummy on each exhalation.

(3) After a while the massage can be changed to a circular (clockwise) motion.

Herbal relaxants and Bach remedies (homoeopathic flower essences which help to ease negative emotional states) can either be used each day, or as fertile times approach. Chamomile tea helps greatly to soothe the nerves.

Energy levels are raised, relaxed and given positivity by enjoyment. Joy is the most important emotion, but often difficult to experience if conception has repeatedly failed. In cases where infertility is long-standing and causing depression, it is perhaps inadvisable to build one's hopes too high each month. My suggestion is that it is desirable to celebrate the *chance* to conceive, rather than its certain outcome, if this is likely to result in great disappointment. However, approaching each attempt as a new chance, and celebrating this in some way, will help to raise joy and optimism, both of which will help towards a positive outcome.

Candle-lit dinners, going out to the movies, moonlit walks by the sea, or any intimate and enjoyable activity will help to set the mood. If alcohol relaxes, a glass of wine won't hurt. "Whatever turns you on" could be the motto for this time.

Responsibilities shelved, other children farmed out to friends or relatives, time off work, all these measures can help. If the home environment is too reminiscent of past failures, use another room or go away for the night or even a couple of days. The keynote is to relax and be joyful and optimistic.

Psychological blocks to fertility are very real. In some cases there can be a deep fear of pregnancy originating in childhood, or if you believe in reincarnation, another lifetime. These may need the expert help of a therapist to uncover and release. However it isn't always that complex. Infertility is in itself so stressful an experience that what starts out as a low level of physical fertility can become a psychologically based problem. High levels of tension and stress affect the adrenals and they in turn affect the hormonal system. High levels of stress and anxiety can be treated well by hypnotherapy and relaxation techniques, herbal and homoeopathic remedies, acupuncture, massage and Bach remedies. It's certainly not necessary to use all of these, and everyone has a preference. Regular exercise is also a great way to reduce stress, as is sex.

Many couples who are continually trying to conceive lose touch with any other aspect of their sex lives. Sexual activity becomes a duty, and associated with negative results and disappointment. Not only does this deprive the couple of the de-stressing effect of sexual activity, but also of much of their loving support for each other. It is as important to identify the *infertile* times in a cycle as the fertile. Then these can be used for intimate and loving expressions of support and trust in the private relationship that is to go on and endure whether the longed-for children come or not.

It is perhaps also of great importance to look at how the relationship will hold together and develop if infertility persists. Although many cases will respond to care and treatment, there will always be some that don't. Infertility is becoming a huge issue these days, with enormous amounts of money being poured into medical research. The reasons for this are many. Lifestyle, poor nutrition, stress, sexually transmitted diseases, environmental pollutants and the negative after-effects of contraception techniques such as the pill and the I.U.D. all contribute.

Although on a global scale one can argue that we have enough children, it remains an immense personal tragedy for those who find, on deciding to start a family, that they can't. For some of these people there will be no final breakthrough. Every couple with a fertility problem has a chance of not solving it. The fact that they have taken it upon themselves to understand and take control of the situation will help most couple's level of acceptance if this proves to be the case, and there will be less likelihood of blame and guilt ruining any chance of changing life direction in a positive way.

In some cases, however, the fear of not ever having a child becomes in itself such a cause of stress, that it can become part of the problem. For these people it may be necessary to sit down and acknowledge the advantages of a life without children (there are many! — more time, more money, more flexibility, more chance to travel, more chance to advance a career, more chance to achieve other life goals etc., etc.). If these can be seen as a real alternative and not just as a failure, then some of the fear and stress may be removed (and the conception facilitated).

Of course for many couples the reasons for infertility are physical and well-known. Let us look at some of them.

Hormonal Imbalance
This can result from past use of the pill, malnutrition (including fasting), stress, past diseases or medication and many other causes, resulting in a lack of ovulation, problems with the length of the luteal phase, or with maintaining a pregnancy amongst other possibilities. The problem can be with the ovary, the pituitary gland or the thyroid gland, and is medically treated with drugs such as progesterone, or oestrogen-like drugs such as *Clomid*. These sometimes have quite drastic effects. Natural and holistic therapies are designed to improve the natural functioning of the glands themselves, rather than the drug itself having the effect. This way the benefits are not detracted from by possible side effects, such as multiple births.

Amenorrhoea
This condition of no menstrual periods can sometimes be the result of hormonal imbalance, or of poor nutrition (notably not enough protein), stress or too much athletic activity. A certain minimum level of body fat (17% to commence menstruation at puberty and 22% to main regular periods, support pregnancy and lactation after 16 years of age) is necessary. Treatment can be with emmenogogues (to promote bleeding), combined with ovarian and uterine tonic herbs, or with many different natural therapies.

Lack of Ovulation
This condition of anovular cycles is not always accompanied by amenorrhoea. Menstruation can occur even though ovulation hasn't, though the reverse is not true and ovulation will practically always result in menstruation, with the notable exception of conception and pregnancy. Lack of ovulation is medically treated with drugs. Holistic treatment would include looking at the diet, stress tolerance, and physical health and correcting *all* of these. Ovarian tonic herbs would include

Chaste Tree, False and True Unicorn Roots, Life Root, Saw Palmetto, and Black Willow.

Problems with Mucous Production
If the cervical mucous is too thick, then sperm cannot penetrate it. This can be caused by chronic yeast infections, which would need to be treated. If the yeast infection is local to the vagina, it can usually be remedied by using a douche, or a sitz-bath, or by soaking a tampon in the following mixture. The method used would depend on whether the inflammation was external or internal.

4 drops of tea tree oil
2 tablespoons cider vinegar
In 2 litres warm water

The amounts, but not the proportions, can be varied according to the method used. This should be used once or twice daily (according to the severity of the symptoms) until the inflammation has been absent for several days.

If the condition continually recurs, it is highly probable that the yeast infection is systemic, and needs rigorous and long-term treatment to effectively eradicate it, which will include anti-fungal agents taken internally and a strictly yeast-free diet.

In other cases, a problem with the texture of the mucous can be treated by adding zinc and calcium to the diet, and using mucous membrane stimulant herbs such as Golden Seal and Barberry Bark. Some cough medicines have been found to contain a substance Guaifenesin, which thins mucous.

Other mucous problems can be insufficiency, which can arise from cervicitis or cauterisation of the cervix (a medical treatment for cervicitis), or incompatibility with the partner's sperm. Some women produce antibodies against the sperm, and this can be determined by a "post-coital" test, examining the mucous under a microscope within a few hours of intercourse. Condoms are used over a period of time to give the antibodies time to subside, and then discarded for the conception attempt. Another reason why the mucous may be hostile to the sperm is if it is too acidic. This can usually be remedied by dietary measures to decrease the acidity levels in the body.

Ovarian Cysts
The Immune stimulant and anti-viral herbs are useful here, such as Poke root, Thuja and Echinacea, and the ovarian tonic herbs. Cysts may severely impair the proper functioning of the ovaries.

Endometriosis

This is a condition where the uterine lining breaks through into the abdominal cavity, where it builds up each month and then bleeds. It can also cause adhesions, blocking the tubes. Natural remedies can be quite successful.

Blocked Tubes

Previous pelvic inflammatory conditions can leave adhesions, or scarring, which can cause blocking of the fallopian tubes, preventing the passage of the egg down into the womb. This can result from gonnorrhoea, infections resulting from I.U.D.s, and other infections. Tests can be done to determine if the tubes are actually blocked, some of which can be quite painful and others which involve surgery. However it can be important to know. Surgery is really the only remedy unless the adhesions are very small, in which case results may be obtained through natural remedies. Surgery is not always successful.

Age

Most of us get less fertile as time goes on. From the age of 30 fertility can decline, and the many women who these days decide to start their families later on in life may have to make a bit more effort! All the measures outlined in this chapter should be helpful.

Low Sperm Count

See Chapter 4 for details.

In no way is this a complete list of fertility problems, and all infertility problems need special attention and should be treated of course by trained therapists, but the part played by the woman and her partner is of extreme importance, and can be critical in the success of any treatment programme.

For those who use these methods successfully there will be much joy.

For those who employ them and still fail to conceive, there will be the consolation of knowing that they have done all in their power. Though this may be small recompense, it may make the difference between a future full of guilt, remorse and bitterness, and one where life can take new and positive directions.

For those who use the methods to conceive with consciousness there will be a physically, emotionally and spiritually richer experience and a similarly benefiting child.

Above all, no-one can be harmed by using these methods, they can only benefit, and that perhaps greatly.

7 PLANETS, SIGNS AND HOUSES

In this chapter a colleague and friend of mine, Jane Bennett, who is an astrologer, looks at other possible astrological influences on fertility. Everyone's fertility changes from moment to moment, year to year, along with other aspects of their health. Some women's fertility changes from middling to high, others' from high to very high, and some from low to viable. The astrological aspects that influence both the levels of fertility and their fluctuations are those present in the natal horoscopes of both parents and that of the time of conception. These could include the phase of the moon, waxing moon being considered more fertile than waning, the amount of water and earth (fertile elements) in the chart, aspects to and the placing of the Moon, Venus (love), Mars (sexual energy), the fifth house (the raising of children), the eighth house (sexuality), the sixth house (health) and the ascendant and first house (the physical body). Here Jane looks at all of this (and more) and through the case histories of some of my clients illustrates how this can be seen to influence an individual and the experiences they go through.

★   ★   ★   ★

Let's now have a look at a broader astrological framework and the insights it may have to offer us concerning fertility and the myriad aspects of human nature and experience that affect our capacity to conceive and give birth to a healthy child.

In this chapter we will be touching on a very specialised field of astrology, medical astrology (as well as general astrology). In the hands of a suitably qualified health practitioner (for example a naturopath or doctor) the specific health indications of a chart can be a wonderful diagnostic tool, although it is never recommended that astrology be used on its own for diagnosis. The reason for this is that an indication of difficulty in a chart does not necessarily mean the "outcome" will be physical. There are different levels upon which we can experience our difficulties, and the result is physical only when there has been no resolution on any other level. Physical illness or problems tend to be more demanding of our attention and can be less easily ignored, so it is when our conflicts and struggles reach this level we *must* begin to work on them. In this way two people may have a similar conflict indicated in their chart and whilst one may have a chronic back problem the other may work with the issue much more on the emotional level, working to reclaim power and control over their lives and faith in support, with only occasional back twinges.

We will be looking at some charts of people who in some way or another have experienced fertility difficulties. If you have any similarities to their charts do not assume you will have the same problems. The indications for fertility, conception or "family" problems are all present in the charts of these people and they *have had* these problems. However there are always a number of ways these issues can be manifest and of course many ways they can be handled or resolved.

I will briefly explain what a horoscope is and look at the main indications in the chart of fertility and family life.

A birthchart is a two-dimensional representation of the earth and heavens, like a symbolic photograph of that moment in space and time. The energy of the moment you are born, beginning your life as an individual being, imprints you with its qualities, the qualities of the universe. These are then yours to express, reflect and experience during your lifetime. Take a look at one of the charts included in this chapter. The outer circle carries the symbols of the signs and due to the Earth's rotation all twelve of these signs cross any given point on the earth's surface in a twenty-four hour period. Seen from earth the sun passes through the signs in a twelve month period, thus giving us the predictable "Sun Signs". The chart is based on a circle which equates to the Earth. This is broken up into twelve segments called houses, each of which relate to different aspects of earthly life. The symbols of the planets, Sun and Moon appear on the chart positioned between the signs and houses, and in the individual's chart are seen to relate to particular signs and houses. The angles between the planets and certain points on the chart are what we call aspects. There are particular angles that by their presence at the time of birth lend certain qualities to the individual. The whole pattern of planets, signs, houses and aspects is constantly changing and in this way offers a sophisticated map of the individual's personality and life experiences.

Here's a concise overview of the elements that have just been discussed: The planets — these are the active agents, the "verbs" of the chart. They represent the dimensions of experience. The signs — these give a character to the activity, illustrated by the planets, and an overview to the area of experience that the houses speak of. The "pronouns" in a sense. The houses — these act as the "nouns" in describing the areas of our life's experience. The aspects — these provide the connections between the planets and planets, and planets and houses. They are the "adverbs" denoting how various elements are integrated and expressed. Please find at the end of this chapter a very brief explanation of each of the planets, houses, signs and aspects, if you are not already acquainted with them. The names of a few recommended texts for further explanation and study may also be found at the end of this book.

Whilst all the elements in a chart *together* represent the dynamic whole of the individual life, and it is necessary to look at all these elements for a *complete* picture, we may look at some elements that have *particular* influence upon fertility and children. These are:- The *moon* — being to do with capacity to nurture and experience of nurturing (mothering). Hormones, moods, unconscious habits and emotional tendencies also come under the Moon's light. To a lesser extent *Venus* — as our capacity for affection, relationship and loving creativity. *Mars* — as our sexual energy and potent capacity to create and sustain new life. To a lesser extent the *sun* — as our general vitality and lifeforce. The *fifth* house — amongst other things — has to do with children, and carries indications about our experience of having and raising children. The *eighth* house — also has to do with our sexuality and potency. The mysterious power of nature reflected in birth, death and rebirth. The *sixth* house — relates to health generally and can give specific indications of gynaecological or fertility problems. To a lesser extent the Ascendant — which relates to the physical body and can give indications of physical weakness and possible problem areas. Planetary aspects to the Ascendant describe the nature and quality of one's own birth.

Particular signs could be seen as more physically "fertile" than others (others may be more intellectually or emotionally "fertile"). And the synthesis of the whole chart gives indications of quality in all sorts of areas: health, relationship, career, money, spirituality, sexuality, fertility, likely environments, physical characteristics ... Rather than trying to give you the tools to do this yourself here (a rather daunting task!), let's now have a look at some case studies together to give you a sense of what a chart can indicate. All of these cases have been, or are, clients of Francesca Naish, though naturally the names have been changed, and the birth data omitted, to protect the privacy of the clients.

Sally, case notes:
Has had no pregnancies. Came off the pill 9 years ago (was on the pill for 7 years before that) and started trying to conceive. 6 years ago had Endemetriosis which cleared up but left one blocked tube (the other is okay). Cycles are regular and all other tests okay. 5 tries at I.V.F. and G.I.F.T. over the last 3 years. No success. Began treatment with Francesca 15.11.88. Suffering from very bad dysmennorrhoea, successfully treated with herbs. Began using Lunar Phase charts. No conceptions to date.

The primary indications in Sally's chart for fertility difficulties are: 1) Uranus conjunct the Moon in the 10th house; 2) Neptune and Saturn conjuncting Mars in the 1st house; 3) A 90°, or square, aspect between the Uranus/Moon conjunction and the Neptune/Mars/Saturn conjunction; 4) Capricorn on the cusp of the 5th house.

One of these influences on its own would not be so powerful, however together they do indicate a strong likelihood for difficulty with vitality, fertility and consistent capacity to nurture.

Let me explain. (Remember, it is the *combination* of all of these things that tell the whole story. One element does not indicate fertility problems.) The Moon is in

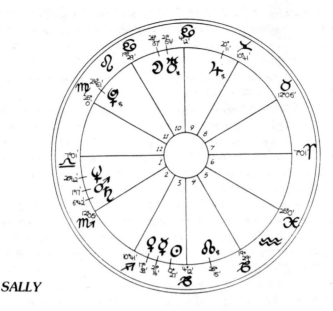

SALLY

Cancer, the sign it rules. Normally this indicates a strong nurturing and motherly emotional nature. In Sally's case this Moon sign certainly gives her the desire to have children, however the conjunction with Uranus adds an erratic and nervy quality to this otherwise "motherly" Moon. Uranus is electric, individualistic, rebellious, unpredictable and undermines the Moon's capacity for consistency, which also means the urge to have children and interest in mothering. A Moon/Uranus person likes to give and care for others of their own free will and can find it very difficult to knuckle down to obliged and dutiful caring. This conjunction does not categorically deny children or indicate that a child's needs would not be met, however it does indicate that thought, planning and "practice" would be necessary for the womb to "hold" the foetus consistently. Uranus requires conscious attention and offers success through awareness. Techniques of visualizing and imaginative *experiencing* of conception, carrying a child to term and successful delivery would be more effective for Sally than a "mechanical-physical" approach. In the 10th house this Moon/Uranus would find satisfying expression working with unusual children with unusual needs, requiring a spontaneous and creative approach *or* as an innovative cook or restauranteur. She would also have a great flair for spacious, fresh and individually tailored interior design.

Overall, Sally is a highly independent woman who needs an avenue for creative and worldly expression (Moon/Uranus in the 10th, Sun in Capricorn, dominance of planets in the East, dominance of planets in Cardinal-initiating, activating-signs, as well as a Cardinal Ascendant-Libra). The conjunction of Mars with Neptune and Saturn indicates some undermining of vital force and difficulty expressing her will and desires in a straightforward manner. This conjunction being in the 1st house thus has a particular effect upon the physical body.

Nevertheless, the planets do not offer opinions of good or bad, and there are ways to achieve the best expression of what we have once we know how. As the natures of Neptune, Mars and Saturn are all so different their combination and expression is complicated, requiring considerable exploration and attention in order to move toward a positive and creative expression of their energy. Saturn is to do with restriction, discipline, responsibility and requires consistent effort. Its effect upon Mars and the 1st house is to restrict vitality, dampening enthusiasm. This often feels like everything is an effort and there is only enough energy for what *has* to be done. On the other hand, Mars/Saturn conjunct especially in Scorpio can give incredible perseverance and determination against all odds. Someone who, once a commitment or decision is made, is capable of achieving the seemingly impossible. The energy missing in vitality is perhaps there in commitment and determination. Neptune is in many ways opposite to Saturn. It is nebulous, ethereal, deceptive, illusory, "spiritual". Neptune can be debilitating to Mars' energy in a way which is hard to pinpoint. Like pulling out the plug of psychic energy, without letting you know why or how. Neptune operates in negatives, so it is only by a process of elimination that you may work out its purpose, maybe. Whilst Mars is egotistic, desire wanting to express itself, Neptune's movement is toward union and dissolution of individuality. Sticky isn't it? It can take quite a bit of learning to get the hang of Neptune/Mars. It takes subtlety, surrender and openness to hearing the quiet voice inside. Then, Neptune/Mars offers great sensitivity to subtle energies, capacity to feel and channel healing and inspiration. The energy will never be robust, yet it can nonetheless be deeply powerful and transformative. Coupled with Saturn there is a capacity to use this energy efficiently and practically. In other words using a limited resource consciously for maximum benefit. Sally would be a hatha yoga, tai chi or swimming person rather than a mountain climber or a netballer.

The 90° aspect between Moon/Uranus and Neptune/Mars/Saturn draws together their influences in a way that provides challenge and conflict. This whole configuration is perhaps the most difficult and challenging area of Sally's life. It demands attention. It "character builds". It provides grist. Sally's fertility difficulties certainly stem from these aspects but so does her desire to overcome them and the incredible process she has already undergone in the name of reproduction. If she wasn't fussed about having kids then there would be little conflict. If she has kids there will be "conflict" in another form. The energy of this conflict does not always have to be dreadful. Once accepted as "her" energy, with myriad outer expressions, it can be experienced as simply a particular quality of life force, and as an energy may become pleasurable (if not quiet or comfortable). Through acceptance and surrender energies like this may be experienced and then used in positive and constructive ways. They are nonetheless unusual and eminently individual, requiring highly personal exploration and resolution, and surrender of concepts of how-it's-s'posed-to-be.

Capricorn on the cusp of the 5th house on its own doesn't mean that much, but in conjunction with these other powerful influences it adds that — there will be restriction and difficulty around having children. If there are children to be born, they will be later in life and few.

Finally, it may well be that through her experience Sally will have something of depth and great value to offer in a broader social context (10th house). Her mothering and nurturing may be expressed impersonally, detachedly and in a socially unusual way. Once attachment to having her own children dissipates other very satisfying expressions may emerge. The quirky nature of Uranus is such that it might be then that Sally carries a successful pregnancy!

N.B. The nature of Uranus and Neptune as outer planets is such that their effect can never be controlled or predicted. We can only surrender to them and hope to learn how to flow with their never usual nor socially acceptable ways.

At the time Sally was contracting endometriosis, transitting Pluto (ie: its current position relative to the birth chart) was beginning a long and strong conjunction (0° aspect) to her Neptune/Mars/Saturn conjunction in the first house. Being in the first house it is very likely that at least part of the effect of this transit be physical and I'm sure there were many other indications in other corners of her life that reflected this transit. Pluto has a dramatic, profound effect and tends to touch us where we are deeply sensitive and in areas over which we have little control. Like the other outer planets (Neptune and Uranus) we cannot control or bargain with Pluto. It is like the power of nature which brings floods and droughts and bush fires. It cannot be ignored and when it is active it completely changes our life. This period of Sally's life would have had a strongly Plutonian flavour, requiring surrender and patience, slowly working through whatever conditions presented themselves and diving as deeply as she could into the experience for whatever pearls may be found. The Pluto/Neptune transit began in October 1981 and continued until September 1983 with varying intensity during that period. However, Pluto then began to aspect Sally's Mars in October 1983 until October 1985, and then began aspecting her Saturn in the same month until October 1987. As Pluto transits these three planets, which in her birth chart are interdependent, we could really say that the whole conjunction, the three planets, is being aspected during that time with emphasis on the particular planet under Pluto's influence.

Of course we mustn't forget Pluto's aspects to the Moon (and by birth connection, Uranus) during the early part of this period, and by birth aspect to the Neptune/Mars/Saturn conjunction, it would also feel Pluto's presence throughout its transit. We could say that the whole Uranus/Moon square Neptune/Mars/Saturn formation described above was put under a major Plutonian assault for the entire period between October 1981 through to October 1987 (or even earlier if we included its aspects to Uranus — beginning October 1979). Once this transit has passed Sally would experience a great lightening, physically and emotionally. Life would somehow feel much easier. She may well have learned through the intensifying of her natal aspects to handle the birth configurations in a more conscious and empowered way, and thus enriched the whole potential expression of herself, illustrated by her chart. If Sally is to have a child, it is much more likely now *and* she may find it is not as important as it was during that long, intense Pluto transit. Life will probably never be as intense and overwhelming for Sally as it was during that period. She will probably just step over her mid-life crisis!

Jaqui, case notes:
Irregular periods before beginning to take the pill when 20 years old. Extreme dysmennorrhoea between pills. One I.U.D. for 6 months. Went off the pill at 30, amennorrhoea (no periods) for the following year. Went on Provena, got periods, then Clomid and fell pregnant on Clomid November '86. The baby died in the womb at about 6 weeks and was carried for 5 months until April '87. No ovulation or period since this pregnancy.

Now that you are more familiar with astrological terminology, let's look at some more cases a little more briefly.

Jaqui's Moon is not strong. It has only one wide aspect to Uranus (an opposition). It is in the sign of Sagittarius and the 9th house, both expansive, outward oriented influences, rather than earthy, focused or nurturing. Uranus doesn't help as we have seen with Sally. At the time Jaqui did become pregnant Saturn was passing over her Moon. Saturn provided the capacity to earth-down, to focus and physicalize energies — however it seems not long enough to bring the foetus to independent life. A Pisces Ascendant has considerable influence over the physical body and would make Jaqui very sensitive to drugs and more mechanical "fertilizing" techniques. Pisces seems to respond better to more

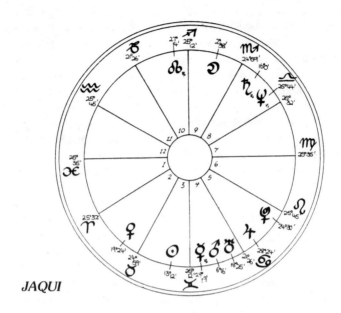

JAQUI

natural and subtle healing techniques, and certainly responds well to spiritual healing, meditation, visualization and suchlike. Jaqui is much more likely to succeed in bearing a child if she embraces a more mystical rather than mechanical approach. She may well find through meditation and/or visualization processes that either deep down she doesn't want a child, or that she opens up a communication with a "spirit" wanting to be born to her, and through this communion alchemizes a conception. (I'm not suggesting immaculate conception, some physical processes are necessary!) Pluto in the 5th house of children indicates the struggle and depths penetrated in the hope or wish for children. I have found invariably that women with Pluto in this position have lost at least one child or foetus, or have had terminations. Of course some women without this formation have had this experience (and there may be a strong indication to the Moon or elsewhere), however those with Pluto in the 5th tend to have a heavier time of it *and* often have more determination to go through the depths to have a child. With the Moon in the 9th, in Sagittarius, and opposite Uranus, Jaqui may well adopt a child or children from overseas (and then perhaps conceive her own). Uranus gives the impersonal, non-physical aspect and the 9th house and Sagittarius the looking toward distant shores for a child.

Susan, case notes:
Trying to conceive October 1985-April 1986. No previous pregnancies. No obvious problems. In consultation with Francesca began using Lunar Phase charts and Sympto-thermal method of ovulation detection. Fell pregnant May 1986. Treated again February 1988 for 2nd child. Fell pregnant June 1988. Used sex-selection techniques both times and achieved desired sex both times. A girl then a boy.

Susan's case history is of someone we would consider has had no real fertility problems. However, a brief look at her chart can perhaps tell us why she chose to seek some professional help and why it was effective so quickly.

A) Susan has the Moon in Taurus, one of the most fertile Moon signs, if not the most. However it is opposite Saturn indicating a tendency to worry and the need to be organized and conscious about conception and child-rearing. For Susan to have Lunar Phase charts and learn to perceive her own ovulation would give her a great sense of control and order. Saturn loves to know where it stands. Similarly, the organization and effort involved in sex-selection techniques would be satisfying to Susan, Saturn giving her the capacity and pleasure in scripting the whole thing. B) Susan also has Pluto in the 5th house, indicating the need to go into the process of life-birth-death-life (especially conception and birth) very deeply rather than be random and vague about it. She would also be a very

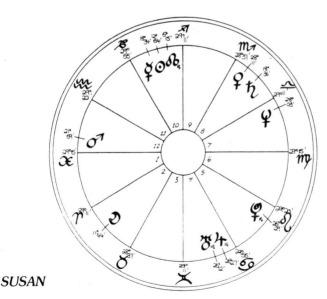

SUSAN

committed mother, even if somewhat emotionally intense. C) Pisces on the ascendant, like Jaqui, with Mars (vitality, desire and potency) nearby indicates the need to approach the physical body subtly rather than mechanically. Simply learning about the Lunar phases, ovulation symptoms etc., would have been a powerful suggestion to Susan's body and psyche, opening her right up to conception. Pisces is very suggestible, and tends to be hurt and damaged by drugs and mechanical interference.

Max, case notes:
Very low sperm count. Partner Mia has had no pregnancies, has normal cycles and tests seem to indicate no fertility problems.

In consultation with Francesca began to use Lunar Phase charts and auto-suggestion techniques to synchronise Mia's hormonal ovulation with Max's Lunar return (ie: her fertile time with his highest sperm-count time). Achieved conception July 1989.

Max has some "difficult" aspects to his Mars (potency). Particularly the opposition (a polarizing influence — energies pulling in opposition directions) between Mars and Jupiter. This is further aggravated by squares from both of these to the Sun (the masculine principle of creativity — ie: insemmination). Jupiter gives great desire to travel, for adventures, to generally stretch

MAX

boundaries more and more. It gives Max driving restlessness, difficult to satisfy.

As far as fertility is concerned this Jupitarian influence spreads his potency far and wide, rather than concentrating it to potent qualities within the body. The Sun's influence in this configuration serves to add restlessness and pull his attention in yet more directions at any one time. Using Lunar Phase charts, and focusing upon them in the desire to have a child, would help to focus Max's energies. Generally learning to focus his energies would be empowering for Max in many ways. His innate energetic habit is to be very restless, to be in many places at once. By learning to focus his attention more he would find he is more potent in more ways than one. At the time Max and his partner conceived Jupiter was passing over his Moon. A peak fertility time for men and women. Jupiter in this case, and particularly in conjunction (empowering) to the Moon, serves to increase the urge to nurture a child (it's a "clucky" time) and greatly increases a person's fertility. Jupiter was strongly conjuncting Max's Moon from July 1st, 1989 to July 19th, 1989.

Frank and Eunice, case notes:
Sperm count very, very low. Eunice, no fertility problems. in consultation with Francesca began using Lunar cycle and herbs. There was a significant rise in sperm count, especially at the Lunar return, more than adequate for conception. Conceived on G.I.F.T. in June 1987.

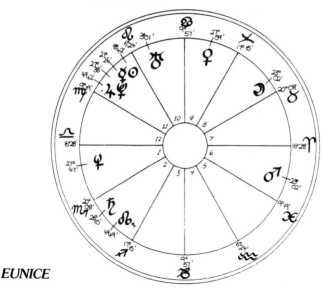

EUNICE

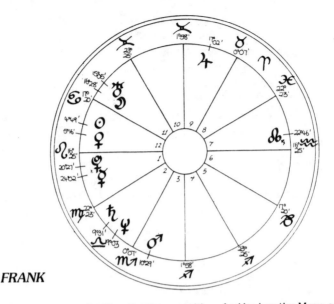

FRANK

Frank also has the Mars/Jupiter opposition. *And* he has the Moon conjunct Uranus. Whilst the Moon would *seem* to be more indicative of female fertility, it still has to do with children and nurturing. Uranus here indicates the unusual, technological means used to conceive, and the Moon/Uranus conjunction in Cancer, as well as all that Leo (Venus, Ascendant, Pluto and Mercury), gives a pretty powerful urge toward having children of his own. During June 1987 Mars passed over Frank's Moon/Uranus contributing much needed vitality and concentration to his fertilizing "potency".

Whilst Eunice had no fertility problems of her own she nevertheless had to go through the "infertility mill" with her partner. She has a happily fertile Moon in Taurus, but with an opposition to Saturn — providing the need to wait, to persevere, to work hard for what would be otherwise natural and automatic. Saturn gives delays and restrictions but when success is finally awarded the Saturnian process makes success so much sweeter. The squares from both the Moon and Saturn to Pluto add a greater depth of longing and emotional struggle, of which the process toward conception was only one illustration.

Lucy, case notes:
Had 4 I.U.Ds altogether. The first I.U.D. perforated her uterus before the first pregnancy, another was lost inside. First pregnancy at 21 years, aborted at 6 months (baby healthy). In October 1986 miscarried at 6 months, baby was dead

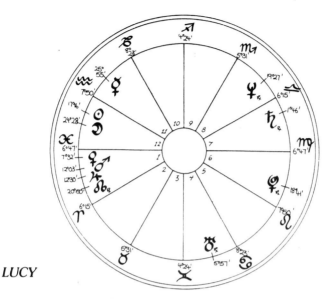

LUCY

since 4 months. No reason given. In consultation with Francesca she fell pregnant within 3 months (May 1987) when her lunar cycle synchronised with her hormonal ovulation.

Lucy has only one planet in an earth sign (Mercury in Capricorn), with a great emphasis in water (mainly Pisces) and Air (mainly Aquarius). She is certainly not an "earthy" person and any mechanical treatment of her body is unlikely to be successful. In this way she had so much difficulty with I.U.Ds. On the other hand, with so much Pisces (especially on the Ascendant) and Aquarius, learning about Lunar Phase and natural conception and contraception techniques would be very uplifting and inspiring to her. The greater sense of her own cycles as part of universal cycles and coming to "feel" when these are (thus feeling to connectedness with all nature) would be bliss to a Pisces/Aquarian. (Aquarius tends toward the unusual, to alternatives, and would warmly embrace knowledge and understanding that offers greater control and choice over one's own body.)

In August 1986, when the baby Lucy was carrying died in her womb Jupiter was passing over the North Node in her birth chart. Jupiter tends to bring out and "exaggerate" (so we don't miss it) the nature of whatever it touches. The Nodes are to do with karma and the path of our soul through this life. As Jupiter activates the North Node some balance is redressed, something cleared and completed, allowing Lucy a clean slate for future pregnancies. As a strong

Piscean, looking for "physical" reasons for the baby's death and consequent miscarriage would have been quite misdirected. With understanding this foetal death and carrying the foetus for a further two months could well have been a healing time for Lucy, perhaps a painful, difficult healing but a deep, deep one, nevertheless.

Lucy, responding well to suggestions for conception with Francesca as well as the positive "hopeful" approach of an experienced professional (providing a mode of intervention she could trust for herself, her body and her child), conceived when Mars positively aspected her Moon — giving her red-blooded strength and emotional fortitude.

Geraldine, case notes:
First pregnancy whilst on the pill — terminated. Another at 28 years old, also terminated. In 1986 had a couple of haemorrhages in between periods, went on the pill as treatment. Also in 1986 discovered lumps in breast and groin. These were present for 3 months before seeing Francesca 28.8.1987. They cleared up, using herbs, after 3 months. Became pregnant first try after lumps cleared up in January 1988.

With the Moon conjunct Pluto in the house of health, in a woman's chart we would expect to see some health difficulties around the periods and reproductive organs. Pluto can be particularly intense in terms of haemorrhages and

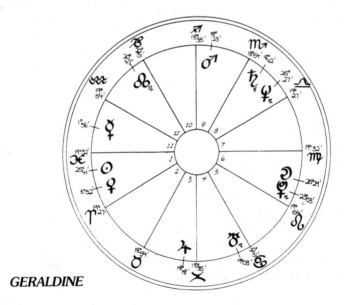

GERALDINE

terminations; Pluto is rarely subtle. As the Moon and Pluto are in Leo they would be rather dramatic but underneath her physical vitality would be pretty good. A woman with the Moon and Pluto conjunct would also experience some very intense mood swings and some powerful "pits". As they are in the 6th house of health these moods are played out on the physical body to a great extent. As Geraldine comes to understand these moods more and is able to "be with" them the physical effect is likely to diminish. Healing techniques of emotional catharsis like rebirthing or psychotherapy could be very useful. Another Pisces Ascendant. Pisceans just seem to be vulnerable to the worst possible side effects of drugs and mechanical treatments. And they respond well to natural methods and positive suggestion. At the time of first seeing Francesca the Sun, Venus and Mars were all passing over Moon/Pluto facilitating a warming, opening, loving and vitalizing effect upon the rather secretive (thus "festering") Pluto influence.

These cases are presented not so much to reach any particular conclusion nor to prove any hypothesis, but simply to illustrate the indications that a birthchart offers regarding fertility. Normally, in an astrological consultation indications such as these would be part of a comprehensive interpretation of the chart. In its *totality* a chart, illustrating the complete person, describes *all* aspects, motivations, energies, struggles and expressions of a person and as such describes perfection. The perfect expression of this person in this universe at this time. In this context, whilst problems of fertility for those wanting to conceive are no less real, they may be seen as a means for growth and understanding, especially when approached in a way that is accepting and creative. This may well be a difficult path to approach with acceptance, however when this is lovingly and gently sought the rewards are as great as the difficulties and may or may not include the birth of a child.

The Basics . . .

Planets:

⊙ Sun — self-expression, creativity
☽ Moon — emotions, habits, nurturance, security
☿ Mercury — communication
♀ Venus — affection, sensuality, sociability
♂ Mars — vitality, desire, assertiveness
♃ Jupiter — expansion, philosophy
♄ Saturn — limitation, restriction, frustration, frameworks
♅ Uranus — shocks, rebellion, universal knowledge
♆ Neptune — illusion, mysticism, universal love
♇ Pluto — death and rebirth, universal power

Houses:

    1st — physical body, initial impression upon the world, quality of dominant environment

    2nd — material resources, money, values

    3rd — day to day communications

    4th — home and heritage

    5th — children, creativity

    6th — work and health

    7th — partnerships

    8th — shared resources and values

    9th — travel, philosophy and study

    10th — career, social role

    11th — community, groups

    12th — inner life, mysteries

Elements and Qualities:

    Fire — dynamic activity

    Earth — productivity, practicality, concrete results

    Air — mental activity, learning and participation in relationships

    Water — feelings, assimilation, regeneration

    Cardinal — new season/initiate

    Fixed — mid-season/substantiate

    Mutable — end of season/transition (toward next season)

Signs:

    ♈ Aries — fire, cardinal, ruled by Mars, symbol — the Ram

    ♉ Taurus — earth, fixed, ruled by Venus, symbol — the Bull

    ♊ Gemini — air, mutable, ruled by Mercury, symbol — the Twins

    ♋ Cancer — water, cardinal, ruled by the Moon, symbol — the Crab

    ♌ Leo — fire, fixed, ruled by the Sun, symbol — the Lion

    ♍ Virgo — earth, mutable, ruled by Mercury, symbol — the Virgin

    ♎ Libra — air, cardinal, ruled by Venus, symbol — the Scales

    ♏ Scorpio — water, fixed, ruled by Pluto, symbol — the Scorpion

    ♐ Sagittarius — fire, mutable, ruled by Jupiter, symbol — the Centaur

    ♑ Capricorn — earth, cardinal, ruled by Saturn, symbol — the Goat

    ♒ Aquarius — air, fixed, ruled by Uranus, symbol — the Water Bearer

    ♓ Pisces — water, mutable, ruled by Neptune, symbol — the Fishes

Aspects:

☌ Conjunction — 0°, unification, concentration of energies

⚹ Sextile — 60°, productive, practical application of understanding

☐ Square — 90°, challenge and construction

△ Trine — 120°, harmony and co-operation, understanding

☍ Opposition — 180°, conflict, controversy, awareness

Use these brief explanations of the planets, houses, signs and aspects to give you a quick insight into the charts and cases offered in this chapter. However for greater understanding it is recommended that you consult some of the many very good books which detail the building blocks of astrology. Several titles are recommended at the end of this book, although there are many others that are more than adequate —

Jane Bennett

Koch houses and the tropical Zodiac were used for charts in this chapter.
Birth data was received directly from the clients and is as accurate as possible.
Naturally names have been changed to protect the privacy of the clients.
Nova, by Astrolabe, was the program used to calculate the charts, on a Toshiba T1200.
Cases were randomly chosen before any horoscopes were drawn, i.e. cases were NOT chosen to "fit" astrological interpretation.

Jane Bennett (B.Soc.Wk., Dip.Astrol., Dip.Hyp.) offers astrological consultations as a form of counselling and healing. She may be contacted through the Village Healing and Growth Centre in Paddington, on (02) 357 5970, or through Francesca Naish. Jane also offers Natural Birth Control and Fertility counselling and charts, for these contact her on (053) 581404.

8 YOUR IDEAL BABY

In a sense every baby is ideal. Not only because we (the parents especially) love them "to bits", but because, as I believe (and you may do too), everyone and everything is a perfect example of themselves, and has a unique and special place and part to play in the unfolding tale of personal and planetary growth. However this need not be interpreted as fatalism, with no place for conscious choice. Conscious choice is very much a part of this process.

If you believe in reincarnation, you may also believe that the characteristics of each "lifetime" are part of our long-term spiritual unfolding. Thus we can learn to accept the dice we are dealt. However that does not mean we are not "allowed" to influence the outcome and try to alleviate suffering wherever we find it, in our own lives or in others. Everything we do influences our life and growth and that of others with whom we are in contact. It is all part of the unfolding. Conscious choice and subconcious desire all merge together into an amazing matrix.

Thus, although some practices can be seen as undesirable in ethical or moral terms, ultimately everything that is done is a direct result of who we are. We just have to keep on trying to refine our choices so they come more and more from unselfish and aware motivations for the "higher" good as we best perceive it.

Thus the doctor who induces birth so he can get away for the weekend, who is acting from selfish considerations, may be doing something which we condemn as "meddling with nature". However, we could also see that the induced birth was part of the baby's necessary experience "in this lifetime". Thus we can accept without condoning, and still fight for better conditions without wasting energy in resentment and regret.

In one sense *every* act is natural, if we see Nature as encompassing human nature and all that occurs in life. This does not stop us choosing what we perceive as the "good" over what we perceive as the "bad". Whilst accepting and embracing the whole of experience, and seeing it as the unfolding of humankind, the earth we live on and our place in the universe, we can still see a necessary role for compassion and the relief of suffering.

So when it comes to choosing your ideal baby it all boils down to this — we can do all in our power to facilitate the arrival of a healthy child with the attributes we perceive as most harmonious for the situation, and still give all of our love to any and all children who are born to us (and to others).

In this chapter we will look at viability of pregnancy and foetus, and sex selection. There can be little dispute that it is preferable to aim for a healthy pregnancy and child. There *might* be some about trying to conceive a child of a particular gender.

Traditionally males have been preferred, to the extent that girl children have been subject to mass murder. In China today, with legislation restricting the number of children allowed in a marriage to one per couple, there is large-scale slaughter of girl babies. Among the Ossets of Central Caucasus the mothers, having retired to their home villages to give birth, would frequently come back empty-handed if not with a boy. Eskimos and Maoris have in their history employed similar "effective" means, and the Radshucmors of India, during the early days of British occupation, killed nearly 10,000 newborn girls every year.

Although this tends to suggest that males would predominate if choice was widely available, it is also clear that a reliable method of selection could help to stop these appalling practices.

The preference for a boy is traditional and stems from reasons as wide as, in the upper classes, a need for an heir, and in the lower classes, a need for a son to help with the work. Although long-held beliefs die hard in a culture, there is reason to suppose that as these concerns become obsolete, and women take a more active part in the world's theatre of events, preferences will even out.

Sex selection can then offer the chance for more balanced families, and more children feeling wanted. A girl who knows that her parents would prefer her to be a boy, or vice versa, has an unnecessary burden in life. As parents choose their children with more success, there will be more love, less rejection and a reduction in family size. Many couples have large families simply as a result of perpetual, but uninformed, attempts to have a son or daughter. In these days of over-population this is not only unnecessary but highly undesirable. In some cases there will of course be more urgent needs to choose the sex of the child, such as when there is a chance of the child inheriting a sex-related disease.

Of course in the majority of cases the preference for a particular sex will not be strong enough (if present at all) to motivate the couple to take any active steps towards regulation. And in some cases the regulation won't work. Although we may increase our success rates at contraception and sex selection, some situations will not respond. My personal belief is that the incoming child should be graciously allowed this small area of choice as to what form it should take, or indeed if it should come at all!

Some situations are also not amenable to the techniques discussed in this chapter, as we shall see. As far as sex selection is concerned, there are a small minority of cases where the choice is not available, the man having an almost exclusively male or female sperm production. Sex selection techniques employed in these cases could result in a failure to conceive at all. In one case a couple who were clients of mine tried for a girl for a very long time, gave up and aimed for a baby instead and promptly conceived twin boys!

As in all situations, it is not so much the availability of the choice which is a problem, but rather the abuses to which it can be put. Our attempts then, should perhaps not go towards suppressing the availability of these techniques but in educating and raising the awareness of the people who may use them. This could result in many other rewards, such as the increase of peace and goodwill worldwide!

All pregnancies should ideally be planned and prepared for. In Chapter 6 we looked at some of the ways in which "conscious conception" can be carried out, and how dietary and health concerns cared for. Now in this chapter we will also look at how to avoid problems in pregnancy for mother and child, and in the health of the foetus.

Although some of the ways we shall discuss will be less "orthodox" and to do with astrology, there is also a place for looking at the more straightforward physiological approaches.

Ever since the discovery, by the Australian Doctor William McBride, of the effect of the drug Thalidomide on the unborn foetus, women have become much more wary of what they do or put into their bodies before or during pregnancy. Most of the practices outlined in Chapter 6 will not only enhance the chances of conception, but also that of the health of mother and child. It is well worth seeing a naturopath or a nutritionist when planning a conception and following their advice throughout the pregnancy. There are also some definite substances to avoid. Excessive coffee drinking has been linked with a tendency to miscarry, and should be brought down to a maximum of one cup a day, or preferably none at all. Smoking during pregnancy has been linked with smaller, less robust children and should definitely be abstained from. Any drug, prescription or not, should be avoided most particularly in the first trimester, and alcohol restricted to the occasional glass of wine, at the most.

Lack of vitamins and minerals is increasingly linked with some birth defects, such as Mongolism (linked with a deficiency in Folic acid and possibly Vitamin E). As we discussed in Chapter 5, the use of the pill and of spermicides can also contribute to deformities.

Stress and anxiety can also greatly affect the healthy course of the pregnancy, and there is of course also the possibility of a pathological condition existing unbeknownst to either the woman or her physician. 5% of all babies born suffer from some genetic defect.

The majority of non-viable infants, however, never reach full term. Nature has her own ways of weeding them out, and many deformed embryos never reach maturity. One out of every 130 conceptions ends before the mother even realises she is pregnant, the defective zygote (fertilised egg) never attaching to the uterine wall, and 25% of conceptions fail to reach an age where they can exist independently outside the womb.

For most women, caring for the health of their bodies, eating well, exercising and staying as relaxed and unstressed as possible, avoiding problem substances, supplementing with desirable vitamins and minerals and eliminating any chance of ill effect from artificial contraceptive methods will be enough to ensure a high probability of a successful pregnancy and healthy child. When there is a personal or family history of problems, it may be necessary to be more cautious. This is where we can look to Dr. Jonas' findings on viability, and though, of course, a medical diagnosis and the options available through orthodox treatment should be explored thoroughly in every case, this is where we leave the area of accepted medical approach.

One woman who appealed to Astra for help after reading about it in the news, was an obstetrician in Prague. She wanted to have a boy. The institute did her chart and calculated which days would ensure the conception of a boy. They warned her that because of unusual configurations in her birth chart it would be difficult for her to carry a child. She ignored the warning, conceived and her pregnancy miscarried. She again enquired if Astra could give her dates for the conception of a full term healthy boy. They sent her the information again and again she miscarried. The institute was concerned and investigated. The Doctor admitted that she had not followed the plan, her scepticism getting the better of her. She then decided, however, that she would try again following the guidelines more carefully.

As we saw in Chapter 2, Jonas' rule number 3 was concerned with viability. The work he carried out in this area, requiring as it did much more time and attention to make the appropriate calculations and conclusions, was much less extensive than that on contraception, or indeed sex selection. Statistically speaking no conclusions can be drawn because of this, and I know of no systematic research carried out since. However the information is, at the least, interesting, and seems to be promising enough to be worth taking into consideration if only in cases where problems have already been experienced.

E.R. Schweighert, of Astra International, as reported in Sheila Ostrander and Lynn Schroeder's Book *Astrological Birth Control*, found the calculations too complex and avoided doing them. I, too, find that the cost of such a service, requiring as it does considerable time, is perhaps unjustified for cases where no problems are anticipated. However in cases where there is a history (family or personal) of problems with either foetus or pregnancy, it would seem to be a reasonable precaution. Jane Bennett, who wrote on astrological indications in Chapter 7, has worked with me before on such cases, and is available for consultation.

The determining factors, as we shall explore, are indicated in the mother's (and possibly the father's) natal horoscopes, in the transits to the natal positions at the time of conception, and the horoscope of the moment of conception.

To examine all these factors, not only is it necessary to draw up several horoscopes, a task which is much faster and easier for us with computers at our disposal than it was for Jonas, but also to determine *in advance* the moment of conception. (This holds for sex selection too.) This means that conception needs to occur on the lunar cycle as it is impossible to predict when the hormonal cycle ovulation will fall. In order not to complicate the situation, it is therefore preferable if the two cycles do *not* coincide, unlike the need in cases of reduced fertility. If by any chance they do so, auto-suggestion techniques can be used as before, but with reverse connotation.

Of course, since the sperm can live for up to 3 days, conception does not necessarily coincide with the responsible sexual act. However, according to Jonas, it can be assumed, for the purposes of viability or sex selection, that it occurs at the exact time of the recurrence of the natal angle, the aspects *at this time* being the determining factor.

Jonas first studied twenty cases of births where the children had been born with some deformity. "It turned out, after I had calculated the astronomical positions at the time of conception (based on the moon phase theory), that all of these conceptions had taken place when the sun and major planets were in opposition. This was a surprising observation" said Jonas, as quoted in *Astrological Birth Control.*

In 1961 in a study of 8,000 births that took place in maternity hospitals in Nitra, Trava, Piestany and Bratislava, Jonas isolated 112 non-viable infants (still-births and those that died shortly after birth), and using the weight and length of the baby to determine the approximate month of conception, and assuming that this took place on the lunar cycle, he calculated the horoscope at the moment of conception and that of the mother at birth. They revealed a characteristic pattern, and Jonas came to this conclusion:-

"During the period of fertility the unfavourable position of the nearer heavenly bodies relative to the sun or the moon and its ruler causes the reduced viability of the conceived offspring, according to the tendencies which are indicated in the woman's birth cosmogram (horoscope)."

In a woman's natal horoscope Jonas identified the problems as being associated with her being born at full moon (180°) and then conceiving at this time (on her lunar cycle).

Although fertility is generally acknowledged to increase with the waxing moon, peak at full moon, and decrease with the waning moon, full moon is also (as we have seen previously) associated with nervous, and perhaps hormonal, instability. More births happen at full moon than at any other time, and it may possibly be a time of incontinence in the womb.

Although I know of no other research indicating a full moon aspect to be associated with problem conceptions, it may be that the electrical potential present at this time (see Chapter 3) could be a factor in the disorganisation of the impulses forming the embryo, as we shall see shortly.

Other considerations in the mother's natal chart which have traditionally been associated with pregnancy problems might include negative aspects to the fifth house or to the moon. This however could also indicate problems with achieving conception, as is illustrated by Jane Bennett in Chapter 7.

The position of the planets at the moment of conception was the other possible cause of viability problems that Jonas isolated. Here he hypothesised that it was the position of the major planets, and their opposition to the sun, that was significant. This same configuration is associated with solar flare activity. Space research shows that at these times of planetary oppositions, sunspots tend to occur, there are shifts in magnetic fields, magnetic storms, cosmic radiation and changes inside the earth. Astronauts avoid moon trips at these times so as not to be killed by solar radiation, cyclones form over the ocean, anti-cyclones over the land, diseases spread in epidemic proportions, the number of icebergs peaks, drought and famine occur and Burgundy wines have vintage years!

Dr. Harold Burr of Yale, whose work I have cited before, showed that all living things are surrounded and controlled by electro-dynamic fields, which give form to the body. Other studies with embryo development have shown that all the cells seem to have the same potential, and the eventual form that they take is determined by their position in the "organising" electro-dynamic field. If a blob of tissue is moved from the leg position to the place where the arm should grow, an arm results. "Kirlian" photography, developed by scientists at the Kirov State University of Khazakhstan, shows these "electronic matrices" on which the physical body is formed. It is observable through this process how solar flares, and other solar system phenomena, affect the energy body.

Also, more research from the space programme shows that subtle magnetic field changes in the earth, that are caused by the sun, moon and planets, actually alter the force field of the human body, and thus the nervous system. Leonard Ravitz, Burr's associate, found that the moon, sun, cosmic and gamma rays, sunspot radiation and other disturbances of the earth's magnetic field had the same effect.

Soviet scientists uncovered an effect of magnetic field changes on the genetic substances D.N.A. and R.N.A., and the two atomic scientists Dr. John Gofman and

Dr. Arthur Tamplin, who wrote *Poisoned Power* state that natural sources of radiation are known to cause mutations in humans. Radiation is also known to affect chromosomes and sperm.

All of this adds up to a convincing argument that certain planetary configurations may have an effect on developing humans. Jonas' theory is clearly in agreement with all this evidence, though there seems to be no particular research which backs up his claim that the moment of conception is crucial. However his calculations have worked well enough in practice to be a major consideration for anyone who feels that they have a tendency to problem pregnancies.

Of course some problems of pregnancy respond well to natural medicines. A tendency to miscarry can be treated effectively by herbal medicines, using the uterine tonic and astringent herbs such as True and False Unicorn Root, Squaw Vine, Wild Yam and Black Haw. Since miscarriage may be nature's way of coping with foetal abnormalities, evidence should always be sought as to the condition of previously aborted embryos, before treatment is undertaken.

Once we have made sure (well, almost!) that the expected child will be perfect — then we can indulge in making it even more so! Sex selection could be seen as an indulgence, though in practice I have found that most people who make efforts to achieve a particular gender in their children do so for quite serious reasons. These may include the desire to avoid passing on a sex-related inherited disease, or because a family is over-supplied with one sex already. There are also those who have a strong preference for more emotional reasons.

The chances of success here are great. We shall discuss 3 basic approaches, all of which claim a very high success rate. Their combination should ensure results in all but the most stubborn cases!

Throughout history there have been prescriptions for sex selection. Though directions have been given on how to conceive a child of either gender, and though the actual spread of the sexes (about 105 boys to 100 girls) is fairly even, given the longer life that women can expect, in most cultures infant women's lib has been a long time coming! The Jewish Talmud declares "when a girl is born, the walls are crying", and several orthodox practices are geared toward male conceptions. The Holy Book of Islam observes that an Arab's face becomes saddened when he hears a daughter has been born to him. The Corribos of South America respond merely by spitting on their wife's bed.

In order to avoid these, or more severe, reactions all sorts of antics have been performed. Exotic concoctions, such as Lion's blood, have been drunk whilst couples adopted crippling positions and performed extraordinary rituals! Ancient Greeks got drunk beforehand, wore boots to bed and tied a string tightly round the right (or left) testicle! Whatever turns you on, as they say. Lying on the right side (for *both* partners!) was believed good for boys, the left for girls, facing north for boys, south for girls (this *might* even have a basis in the geo-magnetic field's effect on chromosomes). In some countries couples take a boy to bed with them on their wedding night, the woman dresses in male clothing, or gets a chance to "tweak" her husband's right (or left) testicle!

However once we gathered a little more information about how the egg and sperm contribute to the conception, things became a little simpler.

The debate through the ages has been on *who* is responsible — the man or the woman? It turns out, fortunately, to be both. Dr. Shettles, of Columbia University's College of Physicians and Surgeons, a pioneer in the field of reproductive physiology whose advice on sex selection will be one of the approaches outlined in this chapter, discovered that there are two types of sperm. One is smaller, round-headed and contains the male-producing Y chromosomes, the other larger oval shaped type carry the female-producing X chromosomes. These mate with the ovum, or egg, which contains another X chromosome, to give XX females and XY males.

In most cases the round (male) sperm, or androsperm, outnumber the oval (female) or gynosperm. There are, in fact, more boys born than girls, but as women live longer this evens out in the end. This "durability" of the female of the species is borne out even at this most elemental level, the female chromosome-carrying sperm being much more resistant to hostile environments (such as the acidic vagina) whereas the male chromosome-carrying sperm are faster and more agile in favourable conditions. However their vulnerability means that although the "male" sperm start out with a considerable advantage in numbers, they end up only slightly ahead, and live only up to 24 hours, whereas the "female" sperm can survive up to 3 days. It's speed versus endurance!

So the male contributes the two types of sperm, and the female the environment which favours one or the other. Although tests may reveal which parent is responsible for single-sex families, in most cases no blame can be levelled at either partner.

In a few cases the male has almost exclusively one type of sperm or the other, and in some cases the woman's mucous or endometrial secretions may favour one sex. This is the basis for Dr. Shettles' procedure for sex selection and may provide a possible explanation for Dr. Jonas' "moon sign" method. It also provides the basis of the dietary approach.

This was discovered by two French scientists, Professors Jean Choukron and Joseph Stolwoski, who, in the early 1980s started getting 95% success by placing the prospective mother on a particular diet for at least a full month before the conception attempt. For those people familiar with the Yin and Yang delineations of food in the Macrobiotic diet, there will be many obvious similarities (Yin is the female force and Yang the male force in ancient Chinese (Taoist) and Japanese (Buddhist) philosophy). Put simply the rule is calcium (and magnesium) for girls and sodium (and potassium) for boys.

The diet is started at the beginning of the cycle *before* conception is attempted, ensuring a full month of correct eating habits. The male partner does not need to follow the diet, though he may choose to do so to be supportive.

Here is a brief outline of the foods allowed and not allowed.

The Boy Diet

Food	Allowed	Not Allowed
Drinks	tea, coffee, fruit juice, cola drinks, mineral and soda water	milk and all drinks containing milk
Meats	everything is allowed	
Fish	most	crabs, winkles, clams, shrimps and cockles
Eggs	sauces, ices, pastries with an egg base	
Dairy products		all forbidden
Bread	all kinds of bread and biscuits without milk	milkbread, pancakes
Cereals	dried cereals and rice	pastries with milk
Vegetables	mushrooms, parsley, artichokes, white haricot beans, dried peas, lentils, soya bean products	green salad, green haricot, spinach, green leafy vegetables
Fruit (fresh)	apples, bananas, dates, apricots, oranges, peaches, cherries	
Fruit (dried and oleaginous)	chestnuts, prunes, dried apricots, dates, dried figs	
Miscellaneous	soups (packet), sugar, flour, honey, jelly, jam, desserts and cakes without milk, margarine, dark chocolate	preparations & sauces with milk or cheese

The Girl Diet

Food	Allowed	Not Allowed
Drinks	weak coffee, apple juice, low-calcium mineral water	coffee, tea, gassy soft drinks, liqueurs, beer, cider
Meats	beef, veal, chicken, turkey, lamb, goose	ham, pork, bacon, preserved, smoked, dried or salted meats
Fish	fish or molluscs in soup	preserved, smoked or salted fish
Eggs	all forms + yolk	
Dairy products	unsalted cheese, Swiss & white cheese, yoghurt, flan	all salted cheese
Bread and Cereals	unsalted bread, biscuits, and home made pastries, rice cakes	salted bread and biscuits, shop biscuits and pastries
Vegetables	green haricots, peas, asparagus, carrots, onions, radishes, cucumbers, turnips, potatoes in small quantities, lettuce	artichokes, mushrooms, celery, beetroot, cabbage, tomatoes, white haricots, dried peas, lentils
Fruit (fresh)	bananas, apples, mandarins, melons, pears	cherries, peaches, apricots, oranges
Fruit (dried and oleaginous)	almonds, nuts, cocoa (limit 2 tspns a day)	chestnuts, dates, prunes, dried apricots & figs, chocolate
Miscellaneous	sugar, flour, jelly, jam, unsalted butter, vegetable oil, margarine, unsalted pastry, spices, herbs, pepper, mustard	shop desserts, cakes & biscuits, salt, olives, pickles, packet soups, mayonnaise, vinegar

Dr. Shettles, who contributed so much to our understanding of how sex selection takes place, advises a more spontaneous approach.

For a female he advocated that intercourse should cease 2-3 days before ovulation, whereas for a male as close to ovulation as possible. This takes advantage of the longer lifespan of the gynosperm, and the fact that the closer ovulation is, the more alkaline and profuse the protective cervical mucous. Interestingly, the Orthodox Jewish practice of avoiding intercourse for one week after menstruation would naturally favour more male conceptions, as intercourse would take place closer to the time of ovulation.

In order to create a more highly acidic environment, favouring the robust female chromosome-carrying sperm, he suggests douching with cider vinegar (2 tablespoons to a litre of water). This immobilises the androsperms. For a male conception the douche should be of two tablespoons of baking soda, which favours the speedier androsperm. Both these douches are harmless to the vagina.

Since the secretions of orgasm are alkaline, if it is experienced at the conception attempt, particularly if it precedes or coincides with male orgasm, it will help the cause of the androsperm. For female children orgasm should therefore be avoided (if possible!). Again the Orthodox Jewish directives are of interest. The Talmud, compiled between the fourth and fifth centuries A.D., contains the following passage.

"The determination of sex takes place at the moment of cohabitation. When the woman emits her semen before the man (meaning she achieves orgasm first), the child will be a boy. Otherwise it will be a girl."

Orthodox Jews do, in fact, have a significantly higher rate of male conceptions than the general population.

Vaginal penetration from the rear is recommended for male offspring, and the face to face or "missionary" position for female. This is one way to ensure deep or shallow penetration, especially important at the time of ejaculation, so that the sperm are either exposed to the acid environment of the vagina (for girls) or safely deposited at the entrance to the more alkaline cervix (for boys).

Abstinence for several days prior to the conception is recommended for boys, none for girls. This is because a low sperm count increases the possibility of a female conception. So — the increased sexual activity required to conceive a girl makes up for not having an orgasm!

It can be seen from above that the more *easily* conception occurs, the more likely it is to be a boy. So couples having certain fertility problems and older prospective parents can expect a higher chance of having a girl.

Dr. Shettles claimed an 80% success rate based on these methods. Combined with other approaches we could expect an even higher result.

Other methods of segregating the sperm have taken advantage of the weight and size differences between the gynosperm and the androsperm.

Centrifuges will separate the sperm because of these qualities, and so will the (rather gentler) process of sedimentation. Sperm taken from bulls was found to produce more females in those cows inseminated later in the day (the heavier gynosperm had settled to the bottom of the container).

In U.S.S.R. Soviet geneticist V. Abroskin concluded from his research that the geo-magnetic field (that of the earth) has effect on the determination of sex. He found that "A particular orientation of the embryo in plants and animals in the G.M.F. in particular periods of embryonic development is important for the determination of the sex of the developing organism."

Back to the hectic antics of the ancients, throwing themselves north and south whilst trying to make love!

"Orientation of the radicle of plant embryos during seed germination toward the G.M.F. north promotes subsequent female sexuality" and vice versa, was his conclusion from experiments on the germination of hemp and cucumber seeds.

It was also Soviet scientists who first explored the "electrophoresis" method of sperm separation, passing the sperm over an electric field, the idea being that the two types of sperm might have different electrical charges. Though the Soviet tests were inconclusive, Dr. Manuel Gordon of Michigan State University got better results in a later trial. When subjected to a mild electric current in a weak saline solution, rabbit sperm tended to separate, the androsperms (male) migrating to the negative electric pole, and the gynosperm (female) to the positive.

It's surprising how often science and ancient tradition mirror each other, The Yin and Yang polarities posited by Chinese philosophy that I mentioned as corresponding to the food classifications in the sex selection diet, apart from representing male and female are also associated with right and left, south and north (possibly the other way round in the southern hemisphere, and associated with polar and equatorial regions), and positive and negative. Traditionally Yin is seen as female, left, north and negative, and Yang the opposite. So far we have seen both ancient ideas and modern research associating male conceptions with right-handed, south-facing, and positively charged (attracted to the negative magnetic pole) characteristics.

Another traditional idea is that the sign of the Zodiac that the moon inhabits at the time of conception is the determining factor for gender. This idea was taken up by Dr. Jonas, in his efforts to explore his Rule No 2, that of sex selection.

As we saw in Chapter 3, the earth's magnetic field is affected by the phases of the moon, and it certainly seems that electro-magnetic charge is a factor in the separation and predominance of male or female chromosome-carrying sperm. Perhaps this is one way in which the moon might affect gender.

Jonas' claim, which complies completely with the traditional astrological viewpoint, going as far back in time as the Egyptian and Alexandrian civilisations, is that when the moon is in a positive (or male) sign of the zodiac, a male child is conceived, and vice versa.

The zodiac is comprised of 12 "signs". These alternate in sexual delineation from Aries (male) to Pisces (female).

The male signs are therefore:-

Aries, Gemini, Leo, Libra, Sagittarius and Aquarius,

and the female:-

Taurus, Cancer, Virgo, Scorpio, Capricorn and Pisces.

The moon travels from one sign to the next in approximately two and a half days. As was the case for the viability calculations, in order to determine in advance which sign the moon will be in at the time of conception, the lunar fertile time is used in preference to the hormonal cycle ovulation, as it can be accurately predicted. Again the time of conception, as for viability calculations, is taken as the exact moment of natal angle recurrence. Each lunar month, when the woman's lunar birthday falls, the moon will tend to be in alternating signs, giving a chance to conceive a girl or a boy every other month. In some months the moon is not "clearly" in a sign at all, being on the "cusp" between two, and these months are better avoided for sex determination. Usually the moon will stay on the cusp for several months in a row, and then revert to an alternating pattern. This can be accurately predicted using astronomical tables (see Chapter 10).

Sex selection was the first of Jonas' theories to be evaluated. As we saw in Chapter 2, he calculated, retrospectively from the birth time and the length and weight of the baby, in which month the conception fell, determined which sign of the zodiac the moon was in at the mother's lunar return, and accurately "predicted' the sex of the child 85% of the time.

According to Rechnitz' calculations, which came up with a similar figure, if the remaining 15% of conceptions were assumed to have taken place at the mid-cycle ovulation, calculated from the woman's last period, then the sex of the child again corresponded to the moon sign present at the time. This would mean that the "astrological" prediction of sex could be, in theory, 100% accurate.

How does this tie in with what we now know about X and Y chromosomes and their preferences? E.R. Schweighert, quoted in *Astrological Birth Control*, comes up with an interesting theory.

He claims that there is evidence that as the moon migrates through the signs of the zodiac, it influences the acidity or alkalinity of the secretions of the lining of the womb. He says "It is not known, however, whether the moon really "determines" or only "indicates" the sex of the child, because the forces that determine this have not yet been discovered. It is only known that the bio-chemical environment of the endometrium is subject to certain periodic variations (alkaline or acidic) and that these in turn lead to a sedimentation of the sperm."

"Animal experiments have been previously conducted in this connection by Dr. Martin Miavec, a doctor of veterinary medicine and university lecturer at the veterinary college in Novi-Sad, Yugoslavia. It was found that the bio-chemical composition of the secretion of the endometrium of cows varied periodically, depending on the moon's migration through a positive or negative section of the eliptic."

In 1940 Dr. William Patersen of Chicago found that the acid/alkali ratio in the blood varied with the lunar cycle of terrestrial magnetism, giving further credence to the idea of lunar influence on acid/alkali balances in the body.

Obviously a woman must be at her mid-cycle or lunar fertile time before she even attempts conception of either sex. Schweighert feels that if the moon is in a "male" sign on this date, and the woman then douches with an acid (vinegar) solution, there will be no conception at all, the sperm with the Y chromosomes (male-producing or androsperm) being hampered by the acid douche, and the female X chromosome-carrying gynosperm failing to survive in the secretions of the endometrium.

"In short," says Schweighert, "conception of the desired sex can only be realised when douching and lunar phases concur, and the woman has an optimal fertile date."

Schweighert claims a 98% success rate using the Jonas sex selection techniques, though recent surveys undertaken by Planetary Eugenics in California, with 800 cases surveyed, give less than 70% results. Certainly there is nothing lost by attempting them, as again, like his methods of contra- and con-ception, they do not affect the body in any way, being dependent on timing only.

Calculations of the sign of the moon at predicted fertile times can be calculated simultaneously with the lunar returns (see Chapter 10). So to use this method merely requires for the couple to abstain from intercourse at the mid-cycle fertile times, and also at the lunar returns until a favourable date, as indicated by their charts, comes along.

This attempt can be accompanied by the process advocated by Dr. Shettles, and preceded by a month of favourable food consumption. This should give an almost infallible sex selection technique, as the success rates quoted for each system separately are impressive enough.

To quote Jonas: "The worst that can happen is that a child is born whose sex is the opposite of what was wished for. However, this has happened before!"

9   SUCCESS STORIES

In this chapter I want to give you some insight into how these methods have worked in individual cases. Some of these case histories have been chosen to illustrate one particular point, and others show a whole variety of inter-relating problems and solutions. Many will demonstrate how a "holistic" approach (one that takes care of all aspects of a case, both physical and psychological), can work so much better than a purely symptomatic treatment.

I have drawn these cases largely from clients seen in my own practice, but also include a few cases of Dr. Jonas' as reported in *Astrological Birth Control* by Lynn Schroeder and Sheila Ostrander. I have naturally not used anyone's real name, though some of the letters to Dr. Jonas are signed and have already been printed in this form.

I have divided the cases into categories according to the effect that I think they demonstrate most clearly, though of course many cases show more than one problem, treatment and result.

It was very gratifying to me, whilst doing the research for this chapter, to see how many women and couples I had been privileged to help. I am so very pleased to have been of benefit and assistance. My thanks go to all my clients past, present and future, for the endless interest and satisfaction I have derived from treating and teaching them, and from seeing how wonderfully women and their partners can manage their own health, fertility and lives.

Conceptions on the Lunar Cycle
Annabelle
Annabelle, who was 23 years old, came to see me 9 months after coming off the pill. She had not had a regular cycle since. At the request of her Gynaecologist she had prepared temperature charts, and from these it did not appear as if ovulation was occurring. The mucous symptoms that she did have, though very scanty, occurred only 7 days before her (occasional) period.

After I had treated her with herbal medicine for 2 months, she had a regular cycle, with normal mucous production and a subsequent period after 15 days. She abstained during this ovulation and the next, but made love during the next lunar fertile time, which came in the second half of her cycle, after her mid-cycle ovulation had already come and gone (as shown by a temperature rise). She conceived, carried the child to term, and gave birth successfully. She came back to me when her baby was 18 months old. She was still breastfeeding, and had not had any periods yet, but was experiencing pain and congestion in her ovaries. I treated her again with herbs, her cycle resumed, and she continued to use the method for contraception.

Joan

When Joan came to see me she had been trying to conceive successfully for 18 months. During that time she had suffered 2 miscarriages, one 13 months before, and the other, which was diagnosed as resulting from a blighted ovum, 5 months after that. She had had no conceptions in the 8 months prior to seeing me. Her history was of a late menarche (onset of menstruation) at 18 years old, and then a vastly irregular cycle over the next few years. She was now 25 and despairing of having a child. She had experience of diagnosing her mid-cycle ovulation, through checking her mucous symptoms and her temperature.

I treated her with herbal medicine, gave her dietary and exercise advice, made a tape for her to use for relaxation and to create positive visualisations of the outcome, and drew up charts showing her lunar phase fertile times. Within 3 months she had conceived, on the lunar cycle, which she had used in preference to her mid-cycle ovulation, which she was adept at diagnosing through long practice but which had not been successful for her. She carried the baby full term and gave birth successfully to a beautiful girl.

Recovery from Miscarriage

In the previous case we saw how Joan recovered from her experiences of miscarriage and produced a healthy child. Another client of mine, Caroline, had similar experiences but we approached the case differently, making viability calculations.

Caroline

Caroline came to see me when she was 39 years old. She had one child of 4 years, who was fine. Since then she had used no contraception. One year before she had conceived, but miscarried at ten weeks. No problems were found with the foetus. She was getting very anxious about time running out for her because of her age.

I treated her with herbal medicine, to promote fertility, the production of healthy eggs and mucous, and to tone up the womb, drew up lunar charts and taught her how to diagnose her mid-cycle ovulation. We used hypnosis to bring her cycles together, and create optimism and patience (a difficult combination!). She conceived within 2 months. However the child didn't develop and she miscarried 2 months later.

This time, because of the problems with the pregnancy and her age, I drew up calculations for viability. A little patience was required again as the viable dates were few and far between. We used hypnosis to create a suitable emotional attitude, and this time to separate the cycles again so we could be sure of the conception time on the lunar cycle.

At the moment she is pregnant, having conceived on her second try, and all is going well.

Conception When Lunar Phase and Ovulation Coincide

Joanna

Joanna came to see me after trying to conceive for only two months. She was impatient. I drew up lunar charts and instructed her in timing and preparation techniques. We made a tape for her to ease stress, create positive visualisations and bring the two cycles together, and gave her tonic herbs. She continued to try for conception for another 6 months, using both the ovulation and lunar times, which occurred separately. During that time by using the tape and auto-suggestions for synchronising the cycles, her lunar and hormonal fertile times crept closer and closer together. At the first occasion when they coincided, she conceived.

Lucy

Lucy had a very bad experience before she came to see me. She was 35, and had just miscarried when 5 months pregnant, the baby having been dead in the womb since 4 months.

When she was 21 she had aborted at 6 months, and though that child had been healthy in the womb, it did not live. No reasons had been given to her for these events, though she had suffered a perforated uterus before her first pregnancy when an I.U.D. lodged in her womb. She had used four I.U.D.s altogether, and one had been "lost" inside her.

She decided against the lengthy process of viability calculations, and learnt timing techniques on the lunar and hormonal cycles. We did some relaxation and visualisation sessions, and she used the techniques herself to bring positivity and synchronise her cycles. Within 3 months her cycles were coinciding and she had conceived. The child was carried successfully to term.

Christine

Christine also had a traumatic history. When she was 24 she had had a termination, which led to continual heavy bleeding and pain in her left side. To solve this she was put on the pill and became very depressed, with headaches and atypical bleeding patterns. However she continued to take it until she was 26, then stopped and became pregnant. Then there was another termination and the insertion of an I.U.D., which should never have been considered, given her history of bleeding. She totally rejected it and had very profuse bleeding.

When this settled an ovarian cyst was found, which was operated on. The operation led to a ruptured bowel and adhesions on the tubes. From this point on she used a diaphragm and her cycle was regular, but with very painful 6-7 day periods. When she was 29 she started bleeding again and was taken to hospital. The adhesions from the previous operation had led to a haemorrhage and the ovary and tube were removed.

After this she had a great deal of hormonal instability for the next year, with bleeding every 2 weeks but no ovulation. Her doctor put her on "Clomid" (a fertility drug). She began to ovulate but became severely hypoglycaemic, came off the drug 3 months later and subsequently had a "normal" period. Then the next period came a week early, she bled for 7 days, and again 4 days later for 2 weeks. She came to me after the bleeding had stopped for 1 week. She wanted not only to "regularise" her menstrual experiences but also to conceive. She felt that this might be impossible given her history. I treated her with herbal medicine and instructed her in timing. She used auto-suggestion techniques on a tape I prepared for her to help control bleeding and make her cycle regular and synchronised with her lunar return. This happened within a few months, by which time her hormonal cycle was behaving itself, and she conceived as soon as the two cycles coincided.

Conception When Lunar Return and Menstruation Coincide

I have already mentioned the Jewish woman who for religious reasons was avoiding sex during her period. She wanted to conceive but had had no success. When I calculated her lunar cycle, it became apparent that it was coinciding with her menstruation. She decided the baby was more important to her than the taboo, and conceived promptly.

Dr. Jonas also had cases like this. One was a couple who had been unable to conceive a child for 7-8 years. Jonas found that the lunar cycle was coinciding with menstruation, which they had avoided, thinking it infertile. Although Jonas gave no specific advice, the couple tried conception during the period anyway and the woman conceived immediately. This was reported by Dr. Farsky, who practises Jonas' methods in Switzerland, to Margaret Lewis. Dr. Farsky claimed many such cases in his own experience.

Jenny
Jenny, a client of mine, corroborated these findings accidentally. She was using the method for contraception, and made love during her period (not really believing she could fall pregnant). She did, and had a termination. Since then her lunar return has coincided with her ovulation, and all is going well.

Other Unwanted Conceptions

Ruth

Ruth came to me after having fallen pregnant whilst using the sympto-thermal method. She was adept at observing both mucous and temperature changes and felt confused and let down that she had conceived, though being scrupulous in her attendance to detail and in following the method. I calculated back to the cycle that she had conceived in, and as she kept comprehensive records of her sexual activity, found that her lunar return had coincided with the only time she had unprotected intercourse that month (believing herself to be "safe").

This has occurred quite often in my experience.

Samantha

Samantha had also been using the mucous method and fallen pregnant. She felt it had occurred during her period, as this was the only time that she had not used a barrier technique for contraception. She wondered if her lunar cycle had fallen then. I calculated, and no, it hadn't. However, whilst asking about her cycle history it became apparent that she often had short cycles under stress. During the cycle that she had conceived in, there had been a lot of upheavals in her life, and it seemed likely that she had ovulated very soon after her period, and the sperm had lived through, fertile mucous being observed as soon as the bleeding ceased. Samantha had a termination and is wiser now!

Kim

Kim had repeatedly conceived whilst using every contraception technique in the book! Twice using a diaphragm, once when a condom burst, once on the pill and once when relying on an I.U.D., as well as 2 more times when using nothing but withdrawal and a rough rhythm calculation. All of these pregnancies had miscarried or been aborted. She felt that she was super-fertile and that nothing would work for her. I explained that however high the levels of fertility, she was still only fertile for a few days each month.

Whilst we were discussing whether she could possibly trust natural methods of birth control, it became apparent that she was, at the least, unsure of her decision to remain childless (she was certainly very attached to the idea of her "super-fertility"!). On further questioning it appeared that these ambivalent feelings had perhaps been the cause of her being a little less than rigorous in applying her contraception techniques. We used hypnotherapy to bring her subconscious desires to awareness so she could deal with them and make a conscious choice that she could stick to. She has used natural methods successfully ever since.

Failure to Conceive Due to Subconscious Blocks

Subconscious psychological blocks to conception can be very real, and sometimes much more complex than the stress reaction experienced by so many infertile couples. The three I illustrate here come from very different causes, but I have little doubt were the main reason in each case for the woman's infertility.

Sandra

Earlier on in her life Sandra had had 2 terminations and these were followed by the premature birth of a child with a congenital brain disorder. She felt very guilty about this, assuming that the terminations had caused an "incompetent cervix" (which may well have been the case), resulting in the premature birth and ensuing disorder. She was suffering from extremely bad dysmennorrhoea, with vomiting, diarrhoea, very heavy bleeding and pain but wanted to conceive again. In this case I feel sure that with viability calculations and psychotherapy her guilt and doubts could have been allayed, and her dysmennorrhoea and infertility healed. However she did not continue treatment with me.

Many people who catch a glimpse of their psychological blocks are alarmed at having to confront them and choose not to. That is up to them. However many use the help of a therapist to bring them to awareness and come to a successful resolution.

Vicky

Vicky was very anxious to conceive. Late in life she had married and was impatient to start a family. When she was much younger she had had two terminations, an I.U.D. had become "jammed" and rejected, and she had been on and off the pill for some years. Her husband's sperm count was lowish (but we soon fixed that!) and she had bad dysmennorrhoea (but we fixed that too!). When she came to me she had been trying to conceive for 18 months. She in fact achieved conception 6 months later but miscarried. Then she admitted to me that she had experienced sexual fantasies involving children for some time and felt extremely guilty about them. When we worked on her acceptance of these fantasies not only did they disappear (sexual feelings feed off guilt) but she conceived quite easily.

Monica

Monica's history was of a very secure childhood, with a father who adored her. There was no apparent physical reason for her infertility, and she could see no possible cause in her very happy childhood memories of her parents as role models. As far as she could see her attitude to parenting was based on the extremely successful relationship she had had with her own parents.

What emerged as she did therapy was a fear that her own husband would form such a strong bond with her daughter (she was sure it would be a girl!) that she would be neglected. Once these fears were addressed and her husband reassured her successfully, she conceived.

Successful Transitions to Natural Birth Control Methods

Megan

Megan had been on the pill for 7 years, had suffered from weight gain, headaches, depression and a host of so-called minor problems. Then she tried an I.U.D. and it perforated her uterus. In despair she turned to the diaphragm, and suffered "toxic shock syndrome", with 24 hours of extreme symptoms for which she was hospitalised. The only time she had felt O.K. about her contraception method was during 18 months of mucous testing, but this had resulted in a pregnancy, which had itself been problematic. The child was 2 months premature, and this after a full month of haemorrhaging.

She suffered quite a lot with her periods, experiencing bad pain, P.M.T., hypoglycaemia (low blood sugar leading to depressed energy states) and lumpy breasts. Herbal and vitamin therapy cleared up the dysmennorrhoea and she embarked on a new contraceptive programme of mucous testing *and* observance of the lunar cycle. She felt symptom-free and confident.

Gillian

Because of painful periods Gillian was put on the pill at 18 years old by her doctor. Later on she became unhappy with this solution and started to use a diaphragm. She was not shown how to use it properly, or how to check that it was correctly inserted, and consequently became pregnant 3 times in one year, with a termination each time. After this experience she went back on the pill, seeing it as the only possibility. However it led to raging "thrush" (or vaginal candida) which drove her to distraction.

After seeing me she came off the pill, used tea-tree/cider vinegar douche, and the thrush abated. She learnt to use her diaphragm properly, and uses it as infrequently as possible, prefering to abstain at her fertile times. She feels physically "terrific" and confidently in control of her own fertility.

Alison

For 15 years Alison was on and off the pill. She felt "bad" when on it, a vague feeling she could express no more succintly. She also, like Gillian, stopped taking the pill, and though she felt much better, used her diaphragm incorrectly and conceived twice. Each time she bled during the pregnancy and terminated it. She then bled almost continuously *for a whole year*, and so went back on the pill and was very worried about coming off it, in case the bleeding started again.

I put her on a herbal medicine mix designed to both eliminate the pill from her system and prevent atypical bleeding. It worked. She feels "So *much* better and in control of my life — it's wonderful!"

Other Effects of the Pill
Helen

After taking the pill for many years Helen decided to start a family. She was horrified when her periods did not resume. She came to me after 8 months' amennorrhoea. With the help of herbs we got her periods flowing. Then it became apparent that she was not ovulating. We fixed that. Then her mucous production seemed almost non-existent and we cured that. Finally she conceived, by using the lunar and hormonal cycles for timing. She was unsure which cycle she conceived on — but she didn't mind!

Leigh

Leigh also had problems after she came off the pill. There was a delay in her cycle returning. When it did there was insufficient mucous being generated around ovulation. This may have been partly an after-effect of the pill usage, but also partly due to the cauterisation of the cervix carried out when she had suffered a cervical erosion (another side effect of the pill).

After treatment and learning to time her hormonal and lunar cycles, she conceived promptly. She then came back to me to help plan her second child successfully.

Other Successful Conceptions
Anne

Endometriosis had blighted Anne's hopes of a pregnancy. She had a severe case with a long history. Again I was able to treat her successfully and when she learnt to isolate her fertile times, she conceived.

Rosemary

Rosemary simply couldn't cope with not being a mother. Her fear that her infertility was a permanent state was causing her such stress that she couldn't sleep and was rapidly becoming extremely run-down. There was no obvious physical reason for her infertility, previously irregular cycles had come good. Relaxation therapy changed her attitude and her ability to conceive. By doing regular relaxation and visualisation she achieved a pregnancy within 4 months.

Judith

For 18 months Judith had been trying to fall pregnant. After 7 months she had a lapiroscopy (when a tiny camera is inserted through the navel and photographs the condition of the reproductive system). This showed enormous fibroids on her uterus, left fallopian tube and a cyst on her right ovary.

Despite these problems, which affected the whole of her reproductive system, she conceived a month later, but miscarried almost immediately. 8 months later she started taking a fertility drug, as she had no mucous production. Still no conception occurred and 2 months further on her quest she came to me. On a strict diet and with the help of herbal medicine we cleared up the fibroids in 4 months, the left tube was clear, the cyst was gone, she had plentiful mucous production and no more painful periods. A miracle. But one more stage to go. 2 more months, 2 years down the track from the beginning of her journey, she conceived, and didn't miscarry. The miracle was topped!

Fiona

Fiona felt herself to be very fit and was extremely puzzled and a litle resentful that her cycles had stopped just when she wanted to conceive. She was athletically active, and ate mostly a raw vegetarian diet. She didn't know that both of these conditions can cause amennorrhoea. When she cut back on her training, introduced more protein into her diet, such as cooked fish, her cycle returned and she conceived.

Stacey

This was an unusual case. There was nothing wrong with Stacey at all. She wanted a child, as she was in a stable relationship and felt the time was right. However, since her relationship was with another woman she had a problem! She had found a willing father, but, because of her sexual preferences, wanted to isolate the fertile time and cut down on the number of attempts! I never heard the outcome, but wished her well.

In Vitro Conceptions

Some women come to me before they try an "in vitro" conception, wanting to avoid it if possible. Some come to "tone up" their system so it has more chance of success. Some come because they find it such a traumatic experience that they feel they can't continue, and others because it has failed them. Despite the great amount of money and publicity that surrounds In Vitro programmes, their success rate is still, on average, only about 10%. Although I am very happy for the successful 10%, I am even more happy that my success rate is better!

Heather

Heather's blocked tubes were caused by adhesions that were so bad that neither surgery nor natural medicines would have been of any use. She had had 3 attempts at In Vitro conception, one time the egg didn't fertilise, and the other times didn't attach in the womb. She wanted to "optimise" her chances for the next try, as she found them somewhat traumatic.

She and I worked together to synchronise her lunar and hormonal cycles and "tone" her reproductive system through the use of herbs, vitamins, minerals and exercise. The next attempt at In Vitro fertilisation took place when her cycles coincided and was successful.

Success From Feeling "In Control"

Geraldine

Geraldine's case has been looked at thoroughly by Jane Bennett in Chapter 7. Her health problems (a history of haemorrhage and lumps in breast and groin) cleared up promptly as soon as she felt she was dealing with them herself in a way that suited her nature and left her feeling good about herself. She then conceived right away.

Sally

Sally's case has also been examined by Jane in Chapter 7. However I have a little to add. Sally's endometriosis had cleared up 6 years before she saw me, but left one blocked tube. She had been on the pill for 7 years, but for the last 9 had used no contraception. However she had not conceived, despite 5 attempts at I.V.F. and G.I.F.T. in the previous 3 years. She also suffered from intense dysmennorrhoea. After 3 months on herbal treatment this had cleared up. Sally still hasn't conceived, but feels so much better physically and emotionally that she doesn't mind so much any more. She would still love to have children, but has learned to accept that this way may not be for her. By feeling that she has done all in her power to resolve her infertility, and not simply handed the problem over to an "expert", she has lost her feelings of resentment, guilt and insufficiency. She has always been involved with the local children, and has scores of them in her house every weekend. So hers is a kind of success story after all.

This end result of Sally's case was not known to Jane when she interpreted her horoscope, but she has picked up on it anyway!

The other case Jane picked as having benefited from feeling "in control" was Susan, who conceived when she felt "organised".

Sex Selection

Susan

The other area of her life that Susan organised well was the sex of her children. Having tried to conceive for 6 months before she came to me, she conceived very promptly, and gave birth to a girl which was what she had planned (using lunar sex selection techniques combined with douching). The second child followed the same pattern, being conceived 4 months after seeing me again (she had been on the pill in the meantime), and being born male, as was desired.

Dr. Shettles gives the following case history in his book (in much more detail).

Bill and Jane Martin

With a family of 5 girls, Bill and Jane felt they could go on trying for a boy no longer. Their marriage had suffered from the guilt and blame that they both had felt. Then they heard of Dr. Shettles' work and visited him in New York. The end result was the longed-for boy that they had almost given up waiting for.

In *Astrological Birth Control* there are several letters from grateful patients of Dr. Jonas' who have conceived a child of the required sex.

M.K. & H.V.

"Dear Dr. It has been 5 months since a healthy son was born to us, according to your calculations. We had especially wished for a son because I am the last bearer of my family name in the republic of Czechoslovakia. I would like your kind permission to keep the calculation which you sent us on Aug 14, 1965, to put it in safekeeping alongside our son Milan's birth certificate."

Mrs X

"After several years of a childless marriage, Dr. Jonas calculated that I could have a child, a son. I will never forget that as long as I live. His prognosis was fulfilled as I gave birth on Nov 6 to a healthy boy".

November 6th was Jonas' own birthdate!

Botlovec

"A daughter was born to us according to your calculations. We are very happy, as she takes the place of our first daughter who died prematurely. We thank you and wish you much further success."

Viera Michaelova

"About a year ago I requested from you a calculation for a girl, as I already had 5 sons. I can now write to you with pleasure that our longed-for daughter, Annie, was born in accordance with your calculations. She is healthy, and a source of great joy to us, for which we offer you our cordial thanks."

Another of Jonas' success stories was the woman obstetrician from Prague who was mentioned in Chapter 8. She got a boy as calculated, after several miscarriages.

Viability

He also had many letters from those women whom he had helped with his "Viability" calculations.

Dr. Orosz Balazsne

"It is with great joy that we take the liberty of advising you that I gave birth to a healthy child, in accordance with your calculations. Prior to that, my children had been still-born. As long as I live, I will be grateful to you for your kindness . . ."

J. Bobcekova

"Words do not suffice to express the joy with which I inform you that after futilely longing for many years to become pregnant and have a child of my own, I have given birth to a son. Whole hearted thanks for this joy go to you, not only in my name, but also in the name of those other women to whom your researches have brought happiness."

Tupka Janosne

"I am writing with a heart overflowing with thanks. My maternal joy is limitless, because I finally have children that are healthy. My first two children were sickly and died prematurely. Your work has produced happiness for me as well as for other women. Thanks again for the information and best wishes for perseverance and health for your further work."

V. Petrovics

Mrs Petrovics of Nitra had given birth to 3 still-born babies in a row, followed by one that was alive but 3 months premature and deformed, and needed constant medical treatment. Jonas found that only 4 times during the year could she conceive a healthy child. She followed the calculations and produced a completely healthy, full-term baby.

Enough for the ladies, let's give the guys a go!

Sperm Count Problems

Max

Max's story has been told by Jane in Chapter 7. He achieved his higher sperm count through using the lunar cycle peak times. His partner, Mia, synchronised her ovulation to his lunar peak with the help of auto-suggestions and a tape I prepared for her.

Frank

Frank was also with Max in Chapter 7. (These guys stick together!) In his case hormonal drugs had had no effect, but herbal remedies combined with vitamins and minerals brought his sperm count up so much, from "very, very low" to "more than adequate", that it was hardly necessary to use the lunar chart. He did anyway, to make sure. His wife had her own fertility problem which made a natural conception impossible, but with the help of the G.I.F.T. programme, Frank's plentiful sperm was used and conception achieved within 4 months of seeing me.

George

George has been mentioned before in Chapter 4. He's the one who wore the wet suit. It took us some time to figure out why he was not responding to the medication he had been receiving, but in the end it was unnecessary to give him treatment. He just gave up surfing in cold weather! Wetsuits keep the testicles hot and under pressure, and so kill sperm.

Andrew

Andrew had a sperm motility problem. We took samples at his "peak" and "trough" times, and it showed a distinct difference. Enough to ensure conception.

Stewart

Stewart has also been mentioned before in Chapter 4. In his case of very low sperm count and motility we combined all the approaches, and he also used some tantric yoga techniques. His count went from 1.8 million (which is low, believe it or not!), to 52 million (which is adequate). These readings were taken at "trough" and "peak" times with treatment in between.

Although I haven't given a separate category to Herbal treatments, it must be very obvious that I consider this an important part of my practice. Although many natural therapies can be successful in cases of infertility, and for some one approach is better than another, my own love is for herbal medicine. I may have been a witch in another lifetime (!), or I may have learnt it all in this one, but herbal remedies have not only fascinated me, but also brought great success to many of my clients, as well as myself and my family.

These stories illustrate many of the points I have tried to make in this book — there are so many others which there is not room for. My thanks to all of them, and to you for your time and attention.

10 CALCULATIONS

As we have seen, the fertile time for a woman on the Lunar cycle, whether or not it coincides with the mid-cycle ovulation, occurs with the repetition of the angle between the sun and the moon (as seen from the earth) at the time of her birth. For a man it is the same.

Let us suppose that Ms XYZ, whose acquaintance we made in Chapter 5, was born when the sun/moon angle was 60°. This occurs about 5 days after the new moon. She will then be fertile, according to Dr. Jonas' findings, 5 days after each new moon, and for a period either side of this peak time. To calculate the natal angle (in this case 60°) the time, date and place of birth need to be reasonably accurately known. As the sun/moon angle increases by approximately 1° every 2 hours the information on birth time does not need to be as accurately known as for, say, a natal horoscope, where the degree of the ascendant, which is the sign of the zodiac rising over the horizon at birth, can change every four minutes. Birth time is valid even if the birth was induced or performed by caesarian section. If the birth took place in a hospital these records are usually still available, although sometimes if the hospital has been closed down or changed its function from maternity, its records may need tracking down, and occasionally may have been lost or destroyed. Most mothers can remember at least an approximate birth time, for example "early morning", which is better than nothing, and in the absence of any accurate information, a noon time is taken and safety margins added to allow for error.

Having established a reasonably accurate time, date and place of birth, astronomical tables can be consulted to give the natal angle, or angle between the sun and moon present at birth. The recurrence of this angle once every lunar month can then be accurately predicted using the same astronomical tables.

The diagram on the next page shows how the angle between the sun and the moon increases during the lunar month, and how the moon looks in the sky at each stage.

At new moon the angle is 0°, as the moon is in a direct line between the earth and the sun, which is why no light is falling on the face of the moon we are looking at, and the moon appears as a very narrow crescent.

5 days later the sun/moon angle has progressed to about 60°, and the moon is a fatter crescent.

By the time the moon is at 90° to the sun we have the first quarter moon (which actually looks like a half moon).

At full moon, the moon is opposite the sun (at 180°) and the whole of one side of the moon is illuminated.

Then the moon cycle progresses to the last quarter of the moon, where the other half of the moon's face appears.

Then, an average of 29½ days after the last new moon, we have another.

A LUNAR MONTH

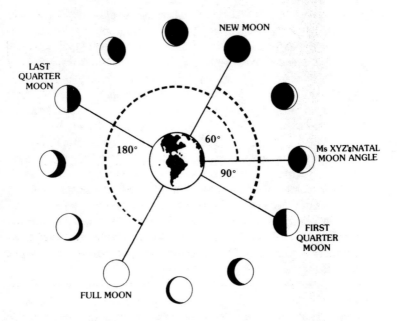

Lunar months are approximately 29½ days long, and this differs from the length of the moon's orbit around the earth, which is approximately 28 days. This is because by the time the moon has completed its orbit, in 28 days, the earth has moved around the sun a little, and therefore is no longer at the same angle to the moon. So the moon has to travel a little bit further to complete its cycle and return to the same position relative to the sun.

So from one new moon to the next is approximately 29½ days, as is the length of time from one full moon to the next. In the case of Ms XYZ it is also about 29½ days from one 60° angle to the next, or from 5 days after one new moon to 5 days after the next.

As a result the moon will be in a different part of the sky (or sign of the Zodiac). This is why a full (or new) moon is in a different sign of the zodiac each month. Ms XYZ's lunar return will also fall in a different sign of the zodiac each month, and whether this is a "male" or "female" sign will determine the sex of the child conceived, according to Jonas' method. This can be calculated from the

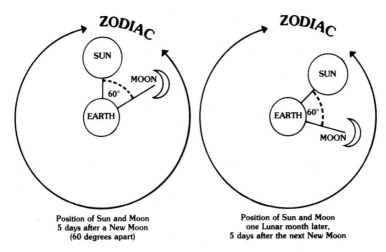

Position of Sun and Moon
5 days after a New Moon
(60 degrees apart)

Position of Sun and Moon
one Lunar month later,
5 days after the next New Moon

astrological tables at the same time as the fertile period is determined. On the charts drawn up for my clients who wish to conceive this is an "optional extra".

This may sound very complicated. All Ms XYZ needs to know, however, is that her peak time is 5 days after the new moon, her natal angle is 60°, and when this occurs each calendar month. She may also wish to know which sign the moon is in at this time if she is interested in sex selection.

Once the return time of this peak fertility has been calculated, safety margins are added.

Originally Dr. Jonas only added 6-hour safety margins after the peak time of each natal angle return. E. Rolf Schweighert of Vienna, who continued research at Astra International after Jonas' work stopped, revised this to 12 hours. The 24 hours before the peak time of natal angle return is considered to be the most likely time for conception to occur, but since sperm can live in the female genital tract for some time in the right conditions, extra margins need to be added for contraceptive purposes.

I have always added the same margins as Schweighert, and found them to be adequate. Sperm have been known to live for up to 5 days in favourable conditions, but are generally considered to be "non-viable" at this advanced age! 3 days is usually considered to be the maximum for viability of conception. Sperm life reduces by a third each day, and 16-18 hours is an average life-span. The number of sperm (sperm count) lowers each day also, and falls below a viable level within 3 days.

Also we need to consider that unless this time coincides with the mid-cycle ovulation then the conditions may not be favourable (such as the fluidity of the mucous) until this situation is (possibly) changed by a spontaneous ovulation occurring within the 24 hours preceding the natal angle return.

If the two cycles do coincide, and fertile mucous is present, then abstinence or precautions would need to be used anyway, for contraceptive purposes.

As a result we have a period of 4 days at each lunar return, made up thus:

4-DAY LUNAR FERTILE INTERVAL

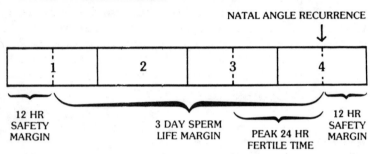

These four days will recur once a lunar month, or approximately every 29½ days. Since a lunar month is shorter than all calendar months except February, the fertile time will fall slightly earlier each calendar month (except March), and every three years or so there will be thirteen in a year instead of twelve.

Remember the lunar phase fertile time remains fertile wherever it falls in the menstrual cycle, *including if it coincides with the menstrual period*.

In fact, as we have seen, coincidence with either mid-cycle ovulation or with menstruation seems to heighten fertility at this time.

So, for contraception purposes the whole 4 day period must be avoided, or precautions taken, and for conception to occur the 24-hour peak time is much the most important.

The 4 day interval will start and end at the same time of day, which will not necessarily be at midnight. Any chart showing these times and dates will be drawn up using a certain time zone, and must be adjusted for different time zones. For example Ms XYZ's peak of 60° may occur at 10 p.m. East Standard Time in Australia, which would be the equivalent of 12 noon G.M.T. in England. Differences in times are always easily ascertained from international telephone operators. Some places also have Daylight Saving Time, which means an hour has to be added. Not that most people will be cutting it that fine! (or that the changeover from fertile to infertile is that immediate).

Calculations to show lunar phase return times and dates can be done by any Natural Birth Control therapist who uses the Lunar cycle as part of the system that they teach. They can also be drawn up by an astrologer, but they may not have the information on the fertility applications, and may just give the exact time of natal angle returns. This leaves it up to the client to add the safety margins, and find out how to combine the information with the use of the sympto-thermal method.

As well as seeing clients for personal consultation, I have offered a postal service for some years, for those who cannot attend in person. All clients, whether consulting directly or by post, receive computer calculated lunar charts for 10 years for contraception, and 3 for conception. These are accompanied by cassette tapes and printed material giving all necessary information on how to use the charts in conjunction with the sympto-thermal method. Although naturopathic and psychotherapeutic treatment can of course only be carried out with those presenting in person, all attempts are made to give advice to postal clients on individual situations where appropriate, and give referrals.

Fees quoted are current at time of publication. Rises, though regrettable, are inevitable with time, in order to maintain a high quality service.

If full payment is accompanied by proof of purchase of this book, then the book price will be refunded from the cost of the service package.

PERSONAL APPOINTMENTS
(Individually for women or couples)

Contraception – 2 initial consultations, 2 hours cassette tape and comprehensive printed material will cover the following topics:

1. Instruction in the detection of fertility in the hormonal cycle through the observation of changing body symptoms and through the use of rhythm calculations.

2. Explanation of, and instruction in, the use of the Lunar phase cycle and individually calculated computer charts giving these potentially fertile times for the next ten years.

3. Instruction in techniques to bring these two cycles into synchronisation.

4. Counselling on contraception techniques for use at fertile times, and their compatibility with fertility awareness observations.

5. Naturopathic treatment for menstrual irregularity or disorders to assist in the use of the method.

Fee $120 (Aus)
Concession rate for unemployed, students etc., $100 (Aus)
Check up appointment advisable after 3 cycles, $35 (Aus)

Conception – initial consultations, 2 hours cassette tape and comprehensive printed material will cover the following topics:

1, 2&3. Instruction in timing as above, to optimise fertility with computer calculated Lunar charts for 3 years (in cases of male infertility charts need to be calculated for both partners).

4. Stress control, Auto-suggestion techniques & Bach flower remedies to overcome psychological problems and regain positivity.

5. Instruction in Lunar and naturopathic methods of Sex Selection.

6. Naturopathic treatment of infertility (male & female).

Fee $120 (Aus)
Concession rate for unemployed, students etc., $100 (Aus)
Additional male Lunar chart $35 (Aus)
Follow up appointments may be necessary if treatment is required.

FOR PERSONAL APPOINTMENTS PHONE (02) 357-5970 OR 357-5988

POSTAL SERVICE

Through the use of cassette tapes and printed material the contraception and conception services are available for those who cannot attend for personal consultation.

Naturopathic treatment (undertaken normally at consultation) will be advised upon and referrals given where possible.

Fee: $100 (Aus) for both contraception and conception.
Concession rate for unemployed, students etc., $80 (Aus)
Male lunar charts (where necessary) $35 extra
Auto suggestion and stress control tape $15 extra

Please note:
PERSONAL CONSULTATIONS HIGHLY RECOMMENDED IF POSSIBLE.

For all postal enquiries please send for application form to:
FRANCESCA NAISH,
VILLAGE HEALING AND GROWTH CENTRE,
208, OXFORD STREET,
PADDINGTON,
N.S.W. 2021,
AUSTRALIA.

BIBLIOGRAPHY

LUNAR INFLUENCES

Astrological Birth Control. Sheila Ostrander and Lynn Schroeder. Prentice Hall, N.J. '72

Women's Mysteries – Ancient and Modern. M. Esther Harding. Harper Colophon Books, Harper and Row, N.Y. '76

The Wise Wound – Menstruation and Everywoman. Penelope Shuttle and Peter Redgrove. Paladin, London '86

Once a Month. Katherine Dalton. Fontana, Glasgow '78

The Mothers. Robert Briffault. McMillan and Co., N.Y. '27

The Determination of the Woman's Period of Fertility and Viability of the Offspring. Eugen Jonas. Nitra '69

New Dimensions in Birth Control. Eugen Jonas. Espress Inc., Wash D.C.

The Fields of Life. Dr Harold Saxton Burr. Ballantine Books

Electrodynamic Theory. Dr. Harold Saxton Burr. Quarterly Review of Biology, Vol 10 '35

The Electrodynamic Theory of Life. Main Currents in Modern Thought Vol 19 '62

Electromagnetic Timing of Human Ovulation. L. Langman and H. S. Burr. American Journal of Obstetrics and Gynaecology, Vol 44 '42

Bio-electric Correlates of the Menstrual Cycle in Women. D. Harold Saxton Burr and L. K. Musselman. American Journal of Obstetrics and Gynaecology, Vol 44 '42

Lunar Periodicity in Human Reproduction – a Likely Unit of Biological Time. Walter and Abraham Meneker. American Journal of Obstetrics and Gynaecology, Vol 77 April '59

Biological Clocks. Frank A. Brown. American Institute of Biological Studies. Stein and Day, Boston '62

Periodic Changes in Electromagnetic Fields. Annals of the New York Academy of Science, '60, '63

Biological Rhythm Research. A. Sollberger. Elsevier, London & N.Y. '65

The Physiology of Diurnal Rhythms. Janet Harker. Cambridge University Press London '64

Biological Transmutations. Louis C. Kervran. Beckman Pub., Woodstock

Shortwave Radio Propagation Correlation with Planetary Positions. R.C.A. Review, March '51

Position of Planets Linked to Solar Flare Prediction. R. Pay. Technology Week, May 15 '67

Man, Weather and Sun. W. Petersen, Charles Thomas, Springfield, Illinois '47

Significance of Air Ionisation. Ivo Pavlick. Medical Climatology. Waverley Pess, Baltimore '64

Periodic changes in Electromagnetic Fields. L. Ravitz. Annals of the N.Y. Academy of Science '60, '63

The Significance of Lunar Phases Theory for the Regulation of Conception. Kurt Rechnitz. Chapters on Scientific Astrology. Pressfoto, Bratislava '69

The Cosmic Clocks. Michel Gauquelin. Avon Books, N.Y. '69

The Scientific Basis of Astrology – Myth or Reality. Michel Gauquelin

Lunaception. Louise Lacey. Coward, McCann & Geoghegan, N.Y.

Body Time. Gay Lear Luce. Temple Smith, London '72 or Bantam

Health and Light. John Ott. Pocket Books N.Y. '76

Supernature. Lyall Watson. Coronet

NATURAL FERTILITY CONTROL METHODS

The Natural Birth Control Book. Art Rosenblum, Aquarian Research Foundation, Philadelphia '76

A Cooperative Method of Natural Birth Control. Margaret Nofziger. The Book Publishing Co., Tennesee '76

The Fertility Question. Margaret Nofziger. The Book Publishing Co., Tennesee '82

The Fertility Awareness Workbook. Barbara Kass – Annese & Dr. Hal Danzer. Thorsons, Wellingborough '84

Natural Birth Control. Katia & Johathon Drake. Thorsons, Well., '84

The Billings Method. Dr. Evelyn Billings and Anne Westmore. Anne O'Donovan, Melbourne '80

The Personal Fertility Guide. Terry Guay. Harbor Pub. Inc., Calif '80

The New Birth Control Program. Christine Garfink and Hank Pizer. Bantam N.Y. '79

ASTROLOGY

The Handbook of Astrology for Australia and New Zealand. Jane Bennett and Craig McIntosh. Greenhouse Pub, Melbourne '86

American Book of Nutrition and Medical Astrology. Eileen Nauman. Astro Computing Services, San Diego

Astrology Inside Out. Bruce Nevin. Para Research, U.S.A.

Alan Oken's Complete Astrology. Bantam N.Y. '80

The Astrologer's Handbook. Frances Sakoian and Louis Acker. Harper & Row N.Y. '73

B I B L I O G R A P H Y

SEX SELECTION

Your Baby's Sex – Now You Can Choose. David M. Rorvik with Ladrum B. Shettles. Bantam N.Y. '71

Influence of Female Genitals on the Development of Sexes. Martin Miavec. Chapters on Scientific Astrology. Pressfoto, Bratislava '69

Boy or Girl Eugen Jonas. Vydavatel'stvo, Bratislava '69